CALIFORNIA

PEARSON LANGUAGE CENTRAL

ELD

PEARSON

Upper Saddle River, New Jersey • Boston, Massachusetts
Chandler, Arizona • Glenview, Illinois

Pearson Language Central Contributing Authors

The following authors guided the direction and philosophy
of English Language Learner instruction and support in
Pearson *Literature*. Their scholarship and advice informed
the development of *Language Central*.

Grant Wiggins

Maria V. Balderrama

Arnetha F. Ball

Danling Fu

Sharroky Hollie

Julie Maravilla

Acknowledgments

Grateful acknowledgment is made to the following for copyrighted material:
English—Language Arts Content Standards for California Public Schools reproduced by
permission, California Department of Education, CD Press, 1430 N Street, Suite 3207,
Sacramento, CA 95814.

ISBN-13: 978-0-13-367446-0
ISBN-10:   0-13-367446-0

7 8 9 10   V011   13 12 11

Grade 6 Contents

Unit 1 How do we decide what is true?

Contents

Grade 6 Contents

Unit 2 Is conflict always bad? 36

Unit 3 What is important to know?

Contents

v

Grade 6 Contents

Unit 5 How do we decide who we are?....138

Grade 6 Contents

How to Use This Book

This book will help you make connections to what you are learning in your English Language Arts class. You will **learn** new vocabulary words, **read** new nonfiction passages, and **practice** language, comprehension, grammar, and writing.

Learn New Vocabulary

Start each lesson with new vocabulary words. Each word has a definition for you to understand. These words connect to the **Big Question** and topics you are studying in your English Language Arts class.

Read a Passage

You will read several nonfiction passages. Each passage has the new vocabulary words you have learned. The passages are also connected to the main lesson topic.

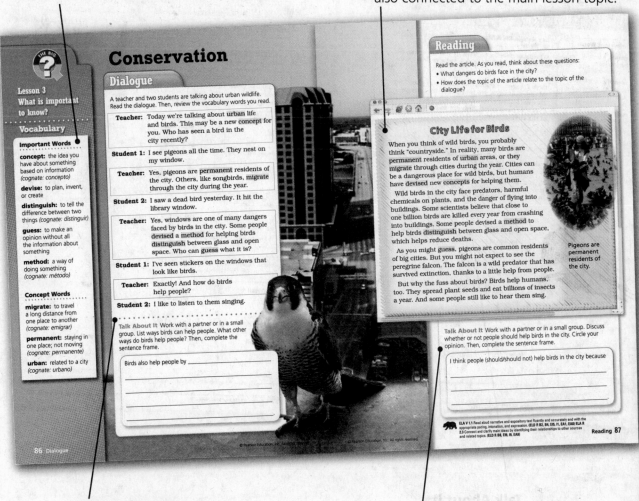

Lesson 3
What is important to know?

Vocabulary

Important Words

concept: the idea you have about something based on information (cognate: *concepto*)

devise: to plan, invent, or create

distinguish: to tell the difference between two things (cognate: *distinguir*)

guess: to make an opinion without all the information about something

method: a way of doing something (cognate: *método*)

Concept Words

migrate: to travel a long distance from one place to another (cognate: *emigrar*)

permanent: staying in one place; not moving (cognate: *permanente*)

urban: related to a city (cognate: *urbano*)

Conservation

Dialogue

A teacher and two students are talking about urban wildlife. Read the dialogue. Then, review the vocabulary words you read.

Teacher: Today we're talking about urban life and birds. This may be a new concept for you. Who has seen a bird in the city recently?

Student 1: I see pigeons all the time. They nest on my window.

Teacher: Yes, pigeons are permanent residents of the city. Others, like songbirds, migrate through the city during the year.

Student 2: I saw a dead bird yesterday. It hit the library window.

Teacher: Yes, windows are one of many dangers faced by birds in the city. Some people devised a method for helping birds distinguish between glass and open space. Who can guess what it is?

Student 1: I've seen stickers on the windows that look like birds.

Teacher: Exactly! And how do birds help people?

Student 2: I like to listen to them singing.

Talk About It Work with a partner or in a small group. List ways birds can help people. What other ways do birds help people? Then, complete the sentence frame.

Birds also help people by _____

Reading

Read the article. As you read, think about these questions:
• What dangers do birds face in the city?
• How does the topic of the article relate to the topic of the dialogue?

City Life for Birds

When you think of wild birds, you probably think "countryside." In reality, many birds are permanent residents of urban areas, or they migrate through cities during the year. Cities can be a dangerous place for wild birds, but humans have devised new concepts for helping them.

Wild birds in the city face predators, harmful chemicals on plants, and the danger of flying into buildings. Some scientists believe that close to one billion birds are killed every year from crashing into buildings. Some people devised a method to help birds distinguish between glass and open space, which helps reduce deaths.

As you might guess, pigeons are common residents of big cities. But you might not expect to see the peregrine falcon. The falcon is a wild predator that has survived extinction, thanks to a little help from people.

But why the fuss about birds? Birds help humans, too. They spread plant seeds and eat billions of insects a year. And some people still like to hear them sing.

Pigeons are permanent residents of the city.

Talk About It Work with a partner or in a small group. Discuss whether or not people should help birds in the city. Circle your opinion. Then, complete the sentence frame.

I think people (should/should not) help birds in the city because _____

ELA V 1.1 Read aloud narrative and expository text fluently and accurately and with the appropriate pacing, intonation, and expression. (ELD R B2, B4, EI5, I1, EA1, EA8) ELA R 2.3 Connect and clarify main ideas by identifying their relationships to other sources and related topics (ELD R B8, EI9, I9, EA9)

86 Dialogue

© Pearson Education, Inc. All rights reserved.

Reading 87

Read a Dialogue

Practice your new **vocabulary** with dialogues. Each lesson will have a dialogue that goes with the lesson topic.

Respond to the Passage

After you read, answer questions about the passage. Then, **practice English** by talking about your answers with your classmates.

9

How to Use This Book

Learn Language and Comprehension

As you become a better reader and thinker, you will need to understand **academic language**—the words of reading and thinking. Each lesson has a page where you can practice this language.

Practice Comprehension

Each lesson will include **charts** and **graphic organizers** to help you to understand what you are reading. They will also help you to record important information.

Language Workshop · FORM FUNCTION

Important Words

detail: a piece of information *(cognate: detalle)*

identify: to tell what something is or who owns it; to recognize or point out *(cognate: identificar)*

key: important

Key Details Key details are words or sentences that help you identify the main idea in a passage.

In the paragraph below, key details are in *italics*; the main idea is in **bold**. Look at how the key details all relate directly to the main idea.

Birds are seen migrating over cities every year. *They spread plant seeds*, which help cities stay greener. *They eat billions of insects* every year that carry disease or harm crops. **Birds are an important part of the environment.**

Talk About It Work with a partner or in a small group. Discuss why it is important for cities to stay green. How does that help make cities nice places to live?

Extend Language Look at the sentences in the passage above that are not in *italics* or in **bold**. Think about how these details may support the main idea. Fill in the chart below.

Detail	How It Supports the Main Idea
1. Birds are seen migrating over cities.	
2. Birds help cities stay greener.	
3. Birds eat insects that carry disease or harm crops.	

© Pearson Education, Inc. All rights reserved.

ELA R.2.4 Clarify an understanding of texts by creating outlines, logical notes, summaries, or reports. (ELD R B8, BW B11, EI9, I12, EAII)

88 Language Workshop

Comprehension Workshop · FORM FUNCTION

Main Idea A web diagram can show how details relate directly to the main idea. Read the passage. Then, fill in the diagram.

In 1970, the peregrine falcon was almost extinct. Some people got together and raised peregrine babies, then released them into urban areas. By 1988, 30 pairs of peregrine falcons were living in several U.S. cities. The cities proved to be great habitats, full of rats and smaller birds to eat. Raising peregrine falcons was sometimes difficult.

Decals, like this one, keep birds from hitting glass windows.

| Detail | | Main Idea | | Detail |
| Detail | | The city is a great habitat for the peregrine falcon. | | Detail |

- Remember, key details are like building blocks that hold up the main idea.
- The main idea is the most important point in the passage.

Extend Comprehension Use the article, "City Life for Birds," to fill in the chart below.

| Detail | Main Idea | Detail |
| Detail | | Detail |

© Pearson Education, Inc. All rights reserved.

ELA R.2.4 Clarify an understanding of texts by creating outlines, logical notes, summaries, or reports. (ELD R B8, B11, EI9, EI10, I10, I12, EAII)

Comprehension Workshop 89

Talk About It

You can practice **discussing** with your classmates what you have learned and how it will make you a better reader and thinker.

G2

© Pearson Education, Inc. All rights reserved.

Learn English Grammar

English **grammar** has many rules. You can practice English grammar for each lesson. This will help you become a better speaker and a better writer.

Connect to Writing

You will write about what you have learned. To help you improve your writing in English, you will write **sentences,** make **outlines,** and write **paragraphs.**

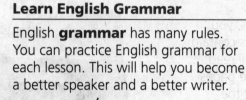

Grammar

Important Word

adverb: a word that describes a verb, an adjective, or another adverb (cognate: adverbio)

Adverbs An adverb is a word that describes or modifies a verb, adjective, or another adverb. Adverbs answer the questions *where, when, how,* and *to what extent.* Adverbs usually end in *-ly.*

Adverb	Purpose	Question
She walked *slowly.*	modifies *walked*	How did she walk?
She is a *very strong* woman.	modifies *strong*	To what extent is she strong?
She walked *extremely* slowly.	modifies *slowly*	To what extent did she walk slowly?

Many birds migrate through urban cities every year.

Extend Grammar In the sentences below, circle the adverb and underline the word it modifies.

1. She watched the birds fly slowly across the sky.

2. Cities can be extremely deadly for birds.

3. The pigeons eat the seeds very quickly.

4. The migration paths for birds can be very dangerous.

5. Peregrine falcons returned steadily.

6. Songbirds are very likely to become confused by artificial light.

7. Many birds live permanently in cities.

8. Importantly, birds help humans.

9. The wolves howled loudly at the moon.

10. The baby elephant carefully put its trunk in the water.

Connect to Writing

Main Idea and Key Details How did you learn to find key details and the main idea? Talk with a partner about what you learned.

Now, write your own paragraph about an animal that lives in the city. On a separate sheet of paper, write what the main idea of your paragraph will be and three key details. Make sure to answer the following questions:

• Is my main idea clear?

• Do my key details relate directly to my main idea?

If you need help, use the sentence frames. The frames will help you organize your ideas.

The main idea for my paragraph will be _____

My first detail is _____

My second detail is _____

My third detail is _____

Writing Tips
Don't forget to
1. make sure your main idea is clear.
2. make sure your key details help support the main idea.
3. go back and revise your writing.

Write a Research Report On a separate sheet of paper, write a research report about how people in the city are trying to protect city birds. What examples can you find about this topic? Try to inform your readers with these examples.

Tips for Your Report
• Ask important questions about your topic. Why do people want to help city birds?
• Include specific facts and evidence to support your report. You can use different sources to research facts. Newspapers, magazines, reliable Internet pages, and encyclopedias all contain facts.
• Use the Writing Process Handbook at the end of this book. This will show you how to draft your story. It will also show you how to record information from other sources. Your report should include a bibliography, or a list of your sources.

Extension Activities

At the end of each lesson, you will explore the lesson topic through **Listening, Speaking, Research, Technology,** or **Writing.** This will help you to think about the Big Question.

An Introduction to Literary Terms

This year in your Reading and Language Arts class, you will be reading many types of literature. These pages contain definitions of the different kinds of literature you will read with your teacher and classmates. You can use these pages during your school year if you have questions about the kinds of literature you are reading.

There are two categories of literature: fiction and nonfiction.

Fiction

Fiction is writing that is imaginative. The main purpose of fiction to is entertain readers. In fiction, the author creates events and characters. Here are some examples of fiction:

Short Stories

Novels

Folk tales

Myths and Legends

Drama

Nonfiction

Nonfiction is writing about real people and events. The main purpose of nonfiction is to inform readers. In this *Language Central* book, you will be reading nonfiction. You will also read nonfiction in your Reading and Language Arts class. Here are some examples of nonfiction:

Essays and Speeches

Diaries

Journals

Autobiographies

Biographies

Talk About It Discuss these questions with a partner or in a small group. What kind of fiction do you like to read? Name a favorite fiction title you have read. What did you like about it?

I like to read _____

Fiction title: _____.

I liked it because _____

_____

ELA LR 3.1 Identify the forms of fiction and describe the major characteristics of each form. **(ELD LR, EI19, EA18)**

Different Types of Fiction

Here are some definitions for the different kinds of fiction.

Type of Fiction	Examples from Your Reading Class
short story a brief work of prose fiction that includes plot, setting, characters, point of view and theme	"Stray," Cynthia Rylant
novel fiction that is book-length and has more plot and character details than a short story	*Time Warp Trio: Tut, Tut*, John Scieszka
myth or legend an important story, often part of a culture's religion or history, that explains how the world came to be or why natural events happen	"Arachne," retold by Olivia Coolidge
folk tale a traditional story that at one time was told orally and was handed down from one generation to another	"The Stone," Lloyd Alexander
fable a short story or poem with a moral (life lesson), often with animals who act like humans	"The Lion and the Bulls," Aesop
drama a story told through the words and actions of characters, written to be performed as well as read; a play	*The Phantom Tollbooth*, Susan Nanus

. . . .

Talk About It Discuss the chart with a partner or in a small group. Why do you think these are good examples of fiction? What is your favorite type of fiction? Create your own chart based on your discussion.

I think these are good examples of fiction because _____

_____.

My favorite type of fiction is _____ because _____

_____.

ELA LR 3.1 Identify the forms of fiction and describe the major characteristics of each form. **(ELD LR B19, EI19, EA18)**

An Introduction to Literary Terms

Different Types of Nonfiction

Here are some definitions for the different kinds of nonfiction.

Type of Nonfiction	Examples from Your Reading Class
autobiography a person's life story, written by that person	"Hard As Nails," Russell Baker
biography a person's life story, written by someone else	"Jackie Robinson: Justice at Last," Geoffrey C. Ward and Ken Burns
diary, journal a daily recording of personal events, thoughts, or private feelings; writing that expresses an author's feelings or first impressions about a subject	*Zlata's Diary*, Zlata Filipović
essay or speech a written work that shows the writer's opinions on some basic or current issue; a speech is a type of essay that can be read aloud and contains language that can inform, entertain, or persuade listeners	"Langston Terrace," Eloise Greenfield

. . . .

Talk About It Discuss the chart with a partner or in a small group. Why do you think these are good examples of nonfiction? What is your favorite type of nonfiction? Create a list of nonfiction titles that you and your partner, or group members have read.

I think these are good examples of nonfiction because _____

_____.

My favorite type of nonfiction is _____

because _____

_____

ELA LR 3.1 Identify the forms of fiction and describe the major characteristics of each form. **(ELD LR B19)**

Poetry and Prose

As you read different types of literature, you will need to know the difference between poetry and prose.

Poetry is a type of literature that usually has rhythm. A poem can use words to create powerful or beautiful images. Some poems have sound patterns, such as rhyme. Most songs are types of poetry set to music.

> There are strange things done in the midnight sun
>   By the men who moil for gold;
> The Arctic trails have their secret tales
>   That would make your blood run cold;
> 5 The Northern Lights have seen queer sights,
>   But the queerest they ever did see
> Was that night on the marge of Lake Lebarge
>   I cremated Sam McGee.
>
>   —Robert Service, from
>   "The Cremation of Sam McGee"

Prose is all writing that is not poetry. Prose can be fiction or nonfiction. Short stories, novels, autobiographies, biographies, diaries, journals, ballads, lyrics, epics, and essays are all examples of prose.

Either Too Young or Too Old

Are you looking forward to your 18th birthday? In many states your 18th birthday marks the day you can get a license to drive, or vote for the first time. Some people think teenagers aren't mature enough to handle these responsibilities before they turn 18. Others who have an opinion on this subject think that it is a misunderstanding, and are calling for a resolution to lower the voting age.

. . . .

Talk About It Discuss these questions with a partner or in a small group. Do you like to read poetry or prose? Why do you like it?

I like to read _____.

I like reading it because _____
_____.

 ELA LR 3.1 Identify the forms of fiction and describe the major characteristics of each form. **(ELD LR EI19, EA18)**

Here is a complete list of the standards that you will be expected to learn this year.

READING

> **1.0 Word Analysis, Fluency, and Systematic Vocabulary Development**
> In this strand of standards, you will use your prior knowledge of word origins, relationships, and context clues—the relationship that a word has with those that surround it—to learn new meanings of grade-level-appropriate words.

Word Recognition

1.1 Read aloud narrative and expository text fluently and accurately and with appropriate pacing, intonation, and expression.

What it means: Reading aloud will help you identify and understand important words and ideas in literary and nonfiction texts.

Vocabulary and Concept Development

1.2 Identify and interpret figurative language and words with multiple meanings.

What it means: Figurative language is more imaginative than the literal, or exact, meaning of words. In grade 6, you will learn how to identify and understand language that appeals to the imagination, and words that have more than one meaning.

What it looks like:
Figurative language: simile
"O my Luve is <u>like</u> a red, red rose
That's newly sprung in June . . ."
—from A Red, Red Rose, Robert Burns

1.3 Recognize the origins and meanings of frequently used foreign words in English and use these words accurately in speaking and writing.

What it means: The English language has many words that come from different languages. Understanding what language a word comes from will help you improve your vocabulary and your knowledge of the English language. In grade 6, you will learn how to use foreign words effectively in your writing and in your everyday speech.

What it looks like:
versus (Latin)
maestro (Italian)
bon voyage (French)
commando (Dutch, Portuguese)

1.4 Monitor expository text for unknown words or words with novel meanings by using word, sentence, and paragraph clues to determine meaning.

What it means: Words can often be understood by their context, that is, through the relationship that a word has with those that surround it. In grade 6, you will learn how to use your knowledge of words, sentences and paragraphs to define unknown words and phrases

What it looks like:
Television's variety becomes a narcotic, not a stimulus. [The previous sentence clues the reader into the meaning of narcotic: something that soothes, like a drug. Its opposite, stimulus, is something that causes one to act.]
—from "The Trouble with Television," Robert MacNeil

1.5 Understand and explain "shades of meaning" in related words (e.g., softly and quietly).

What it means: Many words that may appear to mean the same thing carry slight differences of meaning because of their root word or because of their context—relationship to surrounding words in a sentence or phrase. In grade 6, you will learn how to identify words related in meaning and explain how their meaning differs.

What it looks like:
harsh/rough
firm/solid

2.0 Reading Comprehension (Focus on Informational Materials)   In this strand of standards, you will study grade-level material with an eye for connecting essential ideas, evaluating structure and organization, and applying your knowledge of author's purpose to better understand challenging texts.

Structural Features of Informational Materials

2.1 Identify the structural features of popular media (e.g., newspapers, magazines, online information) and use the features to obtain information.

What it means: News and product information comes in a wide variety of formats. In grade 6, you will learn reading strategies that will help you understand how different news and information texts work, and use your knowledge to find important facts.

What it looks like:
Newspaper: fact-based text

Firefighters in Chicago established the cause of a three-alarm fire over the weekend . . .

2.2 Analyze text that uses the compare-and-contrast organizational pattern.

What it means: When you consider two or more things that are alike in some ways and different in other ways, you are using the skill of comparison and contrast. In grade 6, you will examine texts that use this organizational pattern.

What it looks like:

Squash and racquetball are both indoor racquet sports. Although they are both played on a four-walled court, they differ in speed and racquet size. Squash is played with an inflated rubber ball that has little bounce and racquetball uses a fast, hollow rubber ball.

Comprehension and Analysis of Grade-Level-Appropriate Text

2.3 Connect and clarify main ideas by identifying their relationships to other sources and related topics.

What it means: One way of understanding what a piece of writing is trying to say is by comparing it to other types of writing on the same subject. In grade 6, you will learn reading strategies that will help you understand the ideas of one piece of writing by relating it to similar ideas in another text.

What it looks like:
"The frequency [of non-resonant microwaves] used in microwave ovens (2,450,000,000 cycles per second or 2.45 GHz) is a sensible but not unique choice. Waves of that frequency penetrate well into foods . . ."
—from "How Things Work: Microwave Ovens," by Louis A Bloomfield

"[Our microwave] can accomplish difficult tasks like tempering fine frozen deserts to just the right consistency or preparing seafood dishes that are evenly cooked, yet not overdone."
—Advertisement

The first example uses language that is far more technical than the second example, an advertisement. However, it does give information on how food is heated in a microwave.

2.4 Clarify an understanding of texts by creating outlines, logical notes, summaries, or reports.

What it means: Writing down information will help you understand and remember what you read. In grade 6, you will learn reading and study strategies, such as notetaking, summarizing, and outlining, that will help you be a better student.

What it looks like:

Summary: a restatement of key ideas in your own words

"Now, 93 percent of Chinese households have a television set, and other goods such as washing machines and refrigerators are becoming common as well. But not everyone is benefiting from the changes in China—an estimated 100 million people are unemployed in China's cities and more than 80 million peasants in the country live in poverty, earning less than $100 a year."

—from "Growing Pains in China," Cindy Lin

Even though 93% of Chinese citizens own household goods—washing machines, refrigerators, and TVs, etc.—not everyone is benefiting from the economic changes. Around 100 million people are unemployed in the big cities, and over 80 million peasants in the rural areas have an income of less than $100 annually.

2.5 Follow multiple-step instructions for preparing applications (e.g., for a public library card, bank savings account, sports club, league membership).

What it means: Throughout your life, you will be required to apply for membership to a group or organization or to get some type of service. In grade 6, you will learn how to read different types of applications closely in order to follow their instructions.

What it looks like:

Sports club

To obtain membership, you must do the following:

1. submit written request
2. provide one photo I.D.
3. sign the attached form

Expository Critique

2.6 Determine the adequacy and appropriateness of the evidence for an author's conclusions.

What it means: Facts and examples from a wide variety of sources are used to support a writer's main idea, or thesis. Sometimes, however, the writer does not use enough evidence to support his or her claims or has used the wrong kind of evidence. In grade 6, you will learn how to determine whether the evidence a writer uses is strong enough to support the thesis in question.

What it looks like:

Clear opinion and support

"Letter writing is one of the good things about a civilized society, and it should be encouraged."

". . . A personal letter is a good thing because you can say things that you can't say in a crowd and might not even say to the person face to face. If you feel like it, a letter allows you to take yourself and your thoughts more seriously than you would dare take them in conversation. And you can say things without interruption."

—from "Letter Writing," Andrew A. Rooney

2.7 Make reasonable assertions about a text through accurate, supporting citations.

What it means: Backing up any statements you make about a piece of writing with examples, facts and details either from the text question or outside sources makes it more likely that your points will be taken seriously.

What it looks like:
Quotation

Carbon dioxide has contributed to global warming trends throughout the last century. In his article "Life in the Greenhouse," Michael D. Lemonick states: "Already, humans have increased the concentration of carbon dioxide, the most abundant heat-trapping gas in the atmosphere, to 30% above the pre-industrial levels . . ."

2.8 Note instances of unsupported inferences, fallacious reasoning, persuasion, and propaganda in text.

What it means: Certain forms of writing, such as newspaper editorials and advertisements, often do not have supporting evidence, or the evidence that is used seems questionable. In other instances, the evidence is presented as fact when it is simply the writer's opinion or bias. In grade 6, you will learn how to determine whether a writer's statements are well-supported and whether the support is fact or opinion.

What it looks like:
The city of Buffalo is located in the state of New York. (fact)
Buffalo, New York is a wonderful place to live. (opinion)

3.0 Literary Response and Analysis: In grade 6, you will read and respond to historically or culturally significant works of literature that will both reflect and enhance your studies of history and social science.

Structural Features of Literature

3.1 Identify the forms of fiction and describe the major characteristics of each form.

What it means: Fiction is writing about imaginary characters and events. Its forms vary from poetry and stories to drama. In 6th grade, you will learn these forms and the elements that make them distinctive.

What it looks like:
Short fiction

"There was once a king whose kingdom was plagued by a dragon. The king did not know which way to turn. [He] was at his wit's end."
                     —"Dragon, Dragon," John Gardner

Narrative Analysis of Grade-Level-Appropriate Text

3.2 Analyze the effect of the qualities of the character (e.g., courage or cowardice, ambition or laziness) on the plot and the resolution of the conflict.

What it means: Like a real-life individual, a good character has thoughts, feelings, and even a history. A good writer creates situations for characters to encounter that will make them act or react in a specific way that can determine the storyline or plot: what happens in a story and how it happens.

What it looks like:
"Some believed it was the tattoo, of course, or the fine dark hair coating Dolores's upper lip which kept suitors away. Some . . . fellows couldn't figure out how to court someone who knew more about the carburetor of a car or the back side of a washing machine than they did."
                     —from "A Crush," Cynthia Rylant

3.3 Analyze the influence of setting on the problem and its resolution.

What it means: The setting of a literary work is the time and place in which the story occurs. In grade 6, you will learn how to identify and understand the key elements of setting, and how setting is used to set up character situations in a plot and the resolution of the conflict(s) that arises.

What it looks like:
Influence of war-time on a character's life

"You could not do this and you could not do that. They forced father to wear yellow stars. . . . But somehow we children still managed to have fun. Yesterday father told me we were going into hiding. Where, he wouldn't say."
—from *The Diary of Anne Frank,*
Frances Goodrich and Albert Hackett

3.4 Define how tone or meaning is conveyed in poetry through word choice, figurative language, sentence structure, line length, punctuation, rhythm, repetition, and rhyme.

What it means: Poetry is the most compact form of literature: it pacts different ideas, feelings, sounds and images into a few carefully chosen words. Poetry differs from prose in that it is usually written in verse—language with a definite beat, or rhythm. Tone is the basic attitude or emotional coloring expressed in a poem.

What it looks like:
Tone: surprise and secrecy

"I'm Nobody! Who are you?
Are you—Nobody—too?
Then there's a pair of us!
Don't tell they'd banish us—you know!"
—from "I'm Nobody," Emily Dickinson

3.5 Identify the speaker and recognize the difference between first- and third-person narration (e.g., autobiography compared with biography).

What it means: Every story is told by someone—either by a person or narrator who is not part of the story being told or by a character who is part of the story. In grade 6, you will learn how to identify the narrator and distinguish between the different perspectives or point of view that a story may have.

What it looks like:
"And then, when I had made an opening sufficient for my head, I put in a dark lantern, all closed, closed, so that no light shone out . . ."
—from "The Tell-Tale Heart," Edgar Allan Poe
First person: told by a character who uses the pronoun "I."
"In December 1851, when she started off with a band of fugitives that she planned to take to Canada, she had been in the vicinity of the plantation for days . . ."
—from "Harriet Tubman: Guide to Freedom,"
Ann Petry
Third person: the narrator uses third-person pronouns like "he" or "she."

3.6 Identify and analyze features of themes conveyed through characters, actions, and images.

What it means: In grade 6, you will learn how to determine a narrative's underlying message or insight by noticing details about the elements that make up a story, such as characters, situations and events, and setting.

What it looks like:
Theme: loneliness

I wonder if the elephant
Is lonely in his stall . . .
....
Does he hunch up, as I do,
Against the dark of night?
—from "Pete at the Zoo," Gwendolyn Brooks

3.7 Explain the effects of common literary devices (e.g., symbolism, imagery, metaphor) in a variety of fictional and nonfictional texts.

What it means: In grade 6, you will learn how to identify the various literary devices that appear in a particular piece of work, and use your knowledge of these techniques to explain the underlying meaning of the work in question.

What it looks like:
Imagery
"Early-morning frost sits heavily on the grass, and turns barbed wire into a string of stars. On a distant hill, a small square of yellow appears to be a lighted stage."
—from "Why Leaves Turn Color in the Fall," Diane Ackerman

Literary Criticism

3.8 Critique the credibility of characterization and the degree to which a plot is contrived or realistic (e.g., compare use of fact and fantasy in historical fiction).

What it means: In grade 6, you will learn why some characters and some story lines are believable and why some are not. You will learn how to judge these characters and plots, especially in works of historical fiction.

WRITING

1.0 Writing Strategies: In grade 6, you will write clear, coherent, and focused essays. Your writing will exhibit awareness of the audience and purpose, and will contain formal introductions, supporting evidence, and conclusions.

Organization and Focus

1.1 Choose the form of writing (e.g., personal letter, letter to the editor, review, poem, report, narrative) that best suits the intended purpose.

What it means: Throughout your life, both at home and in school, you will be required to compose a piece of writing for a specific purpose. Whatever the goal of your writing, it will need to take shape both internally with methods of organization, and externally by using various types of writing forms. In grade 6, you will learn how to identify the form that best suits your purpose.

What it looks like:
Job application cover letter

68 Main Street
Anywhere, USA 01000

Mr. John Smith
Personnel Manager, Space Rocket Associates
336 Avenue of the Americas
New York, New York 10036

Dear Mr. Smith:

I would like to be considered as a candidate for the rocket analyst position advertised in The Professional Rocket Analyst on March 5, 2001 . . .

1.2 Create multiple-paragraph expository compositions:
   a. Engage the interest of the reader and state a clear purpose;
   b. Develop the topic with supporting details and precise verbs, nouns, and adjectives to paint a visual image in the mind of the reader;
   c. Conclude with a detailed summary linked to the purpose of the composition.

What it means: In grade 6, you will learn how to write many types of compositions. While compositions can vary widely in form and purpose, they generally consist of the following elements: the introduction, including the thesis statement, the body, and conclusion. To maintain effective unity and coherence throughout your essay, you will learn how to evaluate whether connections among words, phrases, and clauses are clear.

What it looks like:
Topic with supporting details

In seventh grade, I learned that it was easier to make friends if I participated in extracurricular activities. For instance, I joined the Spanish Club and wrote for the school newspaper. Moreover, I joined the football team.

1.3 Use a variety of effective and coherent organizational patterns, including comparison and contrast; organization by categories; and arrangement by spatial order, order of importance, or climactic order.

What it means: Organizing your ideas is an important part of writing. In grade 6, you will learn how best to order your material in various types of writing by using logical methods of organization.

What it looks like:
Order of occurrence

After they located the ancient ship, divers sent a robot down to survey the wreck. Once they spotted the treasure, they prepared for several deep-sea dives.

Research and Technology

1.4 Use organizational features of electronic text (e.g., bulletin boards, databases, keyword searches, e-mail addresses) to locate information.

What it means: The Internet has virtually an unlimited amount of information. In grade 6, you will learn how to find information quickly and effectively by understanding the various options available in search engines.

What it looks like:
Keyword search using the Boolean principle
Topic of inquiry: How does fine music affect babies?
Music AND (intelligence OR learning)

1.5 Compose documents with appropriate formatting by using word-processing skills and principles of design (e.g., margins, tabs, spacing, columns, page orientation).

What it means: Knowledge of your computer means the ability to enter information accurately, format text, use a variety of software, and access the Internet. Much of the information gathered in your research can be organized for speed and ease of retrieval in a database. For comparative analysis, a spreadsheet may be used.

What it looks like:
Word-processing skills: formatting of flyer: font

Does your lawn need a trim?
Call the lawn barber!
555-2555

Evaluation and Revision

1.6 Revise writing to improve the organization and consistency of ideas within and between paragraphs.

What it means: Revision is the stage in the writing when you rework your first draft to improve its content and structure. In grade 6, you will learn how to revise on a global level—sections of a text larger than a sentence that may include central ideas.

What it looks like:
Word choice and clarification

The main character in Rikki-Tikki-Tavi was a mongoose.

In Rudyard Kipling's short story, "Rikki-tikki-tavi," the main character is a courageous mongoose.

2.0 Writing Applications (Genres and Their Characteristics): In 6th grade, you will write various types of essays of 500 to 700 words, using standard American English. You will learn different research, organizational and drafting strategies that will aid you in composing effective essays.

2.1 Write narratives:
a. Establish and develop a plot and setting and present a point of view that is appropriate to the stories;
b. Include sensory details and concrete language to develop plot and character;
c. Use a range of narrative devices (e.g., dialogue, suspense).

What it means: In grade 6, you will master the writing of narratives, including the fictional and the autobiographical, and you will add in such elements as a standard plot line, character development, and other details of story-writing.

What it looks like:
"The girl curtseyed, and sat down. She was very young, and she looked as if she were frightened by the matter of fact prospect the world afforded."
—from *Hard Times*, by Charles Dickens

2.2 Write expository compositions (e.g., description, explanation, comparison and contrast, problem and solution):
a. State the thesis or purpose;
b. Explain the situation;
c. Follow an organizational pattern appropriate to the type of composition;
d. Offer persuasive evidence to validate arguments and conclusions as needed.

What it means: Throughout your academic years, you will be required to write essays that inform and explain different objects and events in a critical manner. In grade 6, you will learn how to come up with a main idea, and support your claim with specific details, examples, and facts.

What it looks like
Cause and effect

The stock market crash of 1929 signaled the start of the Great Depression [effect], which lasted until 1941. The unequal distribution of income [cause] and the falling demand for consumer goods [cause] were contributing factors to the severe economic decline.

2.3 Write research reports:
a. Pose relevant questions with a scope narrow enough to be thoroughly covered;
b. Support the main idea or ideas with facts, details, examples, and explanations from multiple authoritative sources (e.g., speakers, periodicals, online information searches);
c. Include a bibliography.

What it means: In grade 6, you will learn that writing research papers is an integral part of scholarship. This process includes posing questions about a specific topic, researching the question and the topic and finding appropriate examples to support your thesis, and giving credit to the source material you find and use.

What it looks like:
Which major companies rely on demography as a part of their research and development?
Demography: definition: the statistical science dealing with the distribution, density, vital statistics, etc. of population. Webster's New World Dictionary.

2.4 Write responses to literature:
   a. Develop an interpretation exhibiting careful reading, understanding, and insight;
   b. Organize the interpretation around several clear ideas, premises, or images;
   c. Develop and justify the interpretation through sustained use of examples and textual evidence.

What it means: Writing what you think about a work of literature is an important step to overall critical thinking. In grade 6, you will learn how to state clearly your thoughts and opinions on a literary work, and back it with the best possible evidence—the text in question, other texts that deal with your thesis, and examples from personal experience.

2.5 Write persuasive compositions:
   a. State a clear position on a proposition or proposal;
   b. Support the position with organized and relevant evidence;
   c. Anticipate and address reader concerns and counterarguments.

What it means: To get someone to take a particular action or to believe as you do—the art of persuasion is part of your everyday life. Persuasive techniques may take verbal, visual, or written forms. In grade 6, you will learn how to best make your case to a reading audience by learning how to state clearly your opinion, back it up with the best possible evidence, and use memorable and vivid persuasive language.

What it looks like:
Clear position
   "What is needed now is leaders with perspective; we need leadership on a thousand fronts, but they must be men and women who can take the long view and help to shape the outlines of our future."
   —from "The Eternal Frontier," Louis L'Amour

WRITTEN AND ORAL ENGLISH LANGUAGE CONVENTIONS

1.0 Written and Oral English Language Skills: In this strand of standards, you will learn written and oral English language conventions which are essential to mastering listening and speaking skills.

Sentence Structure

1.1 Use simple, compound, and compound-complex sentences; use effective coordination and subordination of ideas to express complete thoughts.

What it means: Varying sentence structure and length in your writing will help you to clarify your ideas and present them in lively and interesting language. In grade 6, you will learn how to coordinate your ideas with and present your ideas in order of degree—subordination— within sentences.

What it looks like:
He bought his mother flowers <u>and</u> chocolates for her birthday.

Grammar

1.2 Identify and properly use indefinite pronouns and present perfect, past perfect, and future perfect verb tenses; ensure that verbs agree with compound subjects.

What it means: Verbs show action or a state of being. The verb forms that help express different times are called tenses. In grade 6, you will learn how to identify and use the various verb tenses and indefinite pronouns—anyone, someone—in your sentences.

What it looks like:
John and Mary <u>will have arrived</u> in Texas by now. As they parted at the airport terminal, Suzy thought: "<u>Anyone</u>, but me!"

Punctuation

1.3 Use colons after the salutation in business letters, semicolons to connect independent clauses, and commas when linking two clauses with a conjunction in compound sentences.

What it means: A writer must do more than set down words on paper; a writer must tell the reader how the words are to be read. In grade 6, you will learn how to give the reader this information by mastering punctuation—a set of standard marks that function as signposts for the reader—such as, the semicolon, colon, and comma.

What it looks like:
Semicolon connects two independent clauses

In the afternoon, she went shopping for cake ingredients; she brought home flour, eggs, baking soda, sugar, milk, and chocolate.

Capitalization

1.4 Use correct capitalization.

What it means: In grade 6, you will learn how to use capitals accurately, such as in the first word of a sentence, for proper nouns and adjectives, in titles of books, poems, stories, paintings, and so forth.

What it looks like:
Oak trees lined the road. (first word of a sentence)
Jane Eyre, "The Road Not Taken" (titles of book, poem)

Spelling

1.5 Spell frequently misspelled words correctly (e.g., their, they're, there).

What it means: Misspellings indicate carelessness on the part of the writer. In grade 6, you will learn spelling patterns, such as "i before e words" and homophones—pairs of words that sound the same, but have different meanings and spellings—that will aid you in correcting misspellings in your work and the work of others.

What it looks like:
Homophones: their, they're, there; too, to, two
"i before e words": chief, relief

LISTENING AND SPEAKING

1.0 Listening and Speaking Strategies: In grade 6, you will learn how to give effective oral presentations: coherent presentations that convey ideas clearly and relate to the background and interests of the audience. You will also learn how to evaluate the content of oral communication.

Comprehension

1.1 Relate the speaker's verbal communication (e.g., word choice, pitch, feeling, tone) to the nonverbal message (e.g., posture, gesture).

What it means: In grade 6, you will learn how to evaluate oral presentations and respond critically and effectively. The main purpose of peer evaluation is to determine which strategies and skills of a presentation were successful and which need work. A secondary purpose in peer evaluation is to apply the successful techniques and skills to improve your own oral presentations.

1.2 Identify the tone, mood, and emotion conveyed in the oral communication.

What it means: In grade 6, you will learn how to understand and evaluate how a speaker feels about his or her subject by listening for key words and phrases that the speaker may emphasize.

What it looks like:

This science fiction movie, though filmed in 2001 and <u>supposedly</u> using the latest technology, <u>looks like a Stone Age reject.</u>

The speaker is being sarcastic in his evaluation of the movie's visual impact. The word "supposedly" and the phrase, "looks like a Stone Age reject," are keys to the speaker's tone.

1.3 Restate and execute multiple-step oral instructions and directions.

What it means: Rephrasing words and phrases that deal with step-oriented tasks is key to doing the tasks correctly.

Organization and Delivery of Oral Communication

1.4 Select a focus, an organizational structure, and a point of view, matching the purpose, message, occasion, and vocal modulation to the audience.

What it means: Speeches can be used for different purposes, such as to persuade an audience to back a particular issue or opinion or to explain to an audience an idea, a process or an object. In grade 6, you will improve your public-speaking skills. You will learn how to use language—informal, standard, or technical— that suits your purpose and is appropriate for the audience.

What it looks like:

Informative speech on a sports car

Audience: teenage boys

You will love this car! It runs 0 to 60 in 3 seconds and reaches speeds of up to 200 miles per hour on professional closed racetracks!

1.5 Emphasize salient points to assist the listener in following the main ideas and concepts.

What it means: Speaking strategies, such as repetition of important points, is key to maintaining the audience's interest in your topic. In grade 6, you will learn how best to use words and phrases to write and deliver effective oral presentations.

What it looks like:

Persuasive speech for class president

I want to be your class president because <u>I like serving the student body, and am more than capable of dealing with your concerns.</u> <u>I have experience in student government:</u> I was class treasurer two years running. I know where to go to get things done! <u>I have experience in student government:</u> I served as your Vice President this year.

1.6 Support opinions with detailed evidence and with visual or media displays that use appropriate technology.

What it means: In grade 6, you will learn how to organize and develop a thesis for oral presentations. The evidence you use to support your claims should be appropriate to your topic.

1.7 Use effective rate, volume, pitch, and tone and align nonverbal elements to sustain audience interest and attention.

What it means: In grade 6, you will learn various verbal and nonverbal strategies that will help you emphasize key points in your oral presentations. This will aid you in delivering effective oral presentations.

Analysis and Evaluation of Oral and Media Communications

1.8 Analyze the use of rhetorical devices (e.g., cadence, repetitive patterns, use of onomatopoeia) for intent and effect.

What it means: Like an essay, a good oral interpretation will take into account important literary tools like repeating patterns and be delivered in lively language. In grade 6, you will learn how to evaluate and make judgments.

What it looks like:
Repetition

"And so if we praise him, our words seem rather small, and if we praise him, to some extent we also praise ourselves."
—from "Eulogy to Ghandi," Jawaharlal Nehru

1.9 Identify persuasion and propaganda techniques used in television and identify false and misleading information.

What it means: To be an informed consumer of information, it is important that you learn to evaluate critically what you see and hear in the media. In grade 6, you will learn how to apply critical viewing skills to the various forms of persuasive techniques used by media and advertising, such as symbols and soundbites, and in turn shape your own informed, unbiased opinions on cultural messages and current events.

2.0 Speaking Applications (Genres and Their Characteristics): In grade 6, you will learn how to deliver well-organized formal presentations employing traditional rhetorical strategies (e.g., narration, exposition, persuasion, description) in standard American English.

2.1 Deliver narrative presentations: a) Establish a context, plot, and point of view; b) Include sensory details and concrete language to develop the plot and character; c) Use a range of narrative devices (e.g., dialogue, tension, or suspense).

What it means: Oral literature existed long before written literature, and storytellers have existed in all cultures. In grade 6, you will learn how to use description, dialogue, and point of view to create interesting characters interacting in a complex world, also of your making.

What it looks like:
Folk tale, establishing plot

"Long ago there was a rich man with a disease in his eyes. For many years, the pain was so great that he could not sleep. He saw every doctor he could, but none of them could help."
—from "We Are All One," Chinese folk tale retold by Laurence Yep

2.2 Deliver informative presentations: a) Pose relevant questions sufficiently limited in scope to be completely and thoroughly answered; b) Develop the topic with facts, details, examples, and explanations from multiple authoritative sources (e.g., speakers, periodicals, online information).

What it means: Informative speeches explain ideas, a process, or a particular object, and they answer questions that an audience may have about a process or product. Often a good amount of research is necessary to cover thoroughly any given topic. In grade 6, you will learn how to gather and present researched topics in the most effective way, distinguishing between your language and ideas and that of the author's. You will learn how to read and use technical language, and how to present information in a clear, and organized manner with the aid of visual representations, such as charts and graphs.

What it looks like:
Source cited: magazine

Antibiotics have been extremely beneficial to humanity. However, because they are so potent, antibiotics also have caused their share of damage. In her article in the March 26, 2001 issue of Newsweek Magazine, Molly Caldwell Crosby states, "that treating every minor infection with a round of amoxicillin [an antibiotic] can harm your health—not by breeding superbugs but by killing friendly ones that live within you."

California Standards

2.3 Deliver oral responses to literature:
  a. Develop an interpretation exhibiting careful reading, understanding, and insight;
  b. Organize the selected interpretation around several clear ideas, premises, or images;
  c. Develop and justify the selected interpretation through sustained use of examples and textual evidence.

What it means: A good oral response to literature is very much like a good essay: it has a beginning, middle and end, draws on the text and other resources for support of a main idea, and uses lively language to elaborate upon the main point and key ideas connected to the thesis. In grade 6, you will learn how to use interpretive reading strategies, essay writing techniques, and oral delivery skills to write and deliver effective oral responses to literature.

What it looks like:

"O Captain! my Captain! our fearful trip
  is done,
The ship has weather'd every rack, the
  prize we sought is won . . .
    But O heart! heart! heart!
    O the bleeding drops of red,
      Where on the deck my captain lies,
      Fallen cold and dead."

So begins the famous poem, "O Captain! My Captain!," that Walt Whitman wrote about the death of Abraham Lincoln. In his poem, Whitman uses the metaphor of the ship of state to talk about the "fearful trip," which was the Civil War, and its fallen leader, or Captain, who was shot just days after Robert E. Lee surrendered to Ulysses S. Grant, the general of the Northern Army.

2.4 Deliver persuasive presentations:
  a. Provide a clear statement of the position;
  b. Include relevant evidence;
  c. Offer a logical sequence of information;
  d. Engage the listener and foster acceptance of the proposition or proposal.

What it means: You will find that you will have strong opinions on issues that arise both in school and at home. In grade 6, you will learn how to construct oral presentations that will help you convince an audience of your position. You will learn how to support your opinions with the best evidence, and how to use verbal and nonverbal strategies to emphasize your message.

What it looks like:

Verbal strategies: parallel structures and repetition

". . . In spite of the difficulties of the moment, I still have a dream. It is a dream deeply rooted in the American dream. I have a dream that one day this nation will rise up and live out the true meaning of its creed: 'We hold these truths to be self-evident: that all men are created equal' . . ."
                    —from Martin Luther King's speech at the
                         Lincoln Memorial, August 28, 1963

2.5 Deliver presentations on problems and solutions:
  a. Theorize on the causes and effects of each problem and establish connections between the defined problem and at least one solution
  b. Offer persuasive evidence to validate the definition of the problem and the proposed solutions.

What it means: In grade 6, you will deliver presentations that focus on a problem, the causes of the problem and the effects it has, and at least one valid solution.

English Language Development Standards Grades 6–8

WORD ANALYSIS...

Beginning

B1. Recognize and correctly pronounce most English phonemes while reading aloud.

B2. Recognize the most common English morphemes in phrases and simple sentences.

Early Intermediate

EI1. Produce most English phonemes comprehensibly while reading aloud one's own writing, simple sentences, or simple texts.

EI2. Use common English morphemes in oral and silent reading.

EI3. Recognize obvious cognates (e.g., education, educación; university, universidad) in phrases, simple sentences, literature, and content area texts.

Intermediate

I1. Apply knowledge of common English morphemes in oral and silent reading to derive meaning from literature and texts in content areas.

I2. Identify cognates (e.g., agonía, agony) and false cognates (e.g., éxito, exit) in literature and texts in content areas.

Early Advanced

EA1. Apply knowledge of word relationships, such as roots and affixes, to derive meaning from literature and texts in content areas.

EA2. Distinguish between cognates and false cognates in literature and texts in content areas.

VOCABULARY DEVELOPMENT.....................................

Beginning

B3. Read aloud simple words presented in literature and subject-matter texts; demonstrate comprehension by using one to two words or simple-sentence responses.

B4. Respond with appropriate short phrases or sentences in various social and academic settings (e.g., answer simple questions).

B5. Create a simple dictionary of words frequently used by the student.

B6. Retell stories by using phrases and sentences.

B7. Produce simple vocabulary (single words or short phrases) to communicate basic needs in social and academic settings (e.g., locations, greetings, classroom objects).

Early Intermediate

EI4. Use knowledge of literature and content areas to understand unknown words.

EI5. Read simple paragraphs and passages independently.

EI6. Demonstrate internalization of English grammar, usage, and word choice by recognizing and correcting some errors when speaking or reading aloud.

EI7. Read aloud with appropriate pacing, intonation, and expression one's own writing of narrative and expository texts.

EI8. Use a standard dictionary to find the meaning of known vocabulary.

Intermediate

I3. Use a standard dictionary to determine meanings of unknown words.

I4. Use knowledge of English morphemes, phonics, and syntax to decode text.

I5. Recognize simple idioms, analogies, figures of speech (e.g., to "take a fall"), and metaphors in literature and texts in content areas.

I6. Demonstrate internalization of English grammar, usage, and word choice by recognizing and correcting errors when speaking or reading aloud.

I7. Use decoding skills and knowledge of both academic and social vocabulary to read independently.

I8. Recognize that some words have multiple meanings.

Early Advanced

EA3. Use knowledge of English morphemes, phonics, and syntax to decode and interpret the meaning of unfamiliar words.

EA4. Recognize that some words have multiple meanings and apply this knowledge to read literature and texts in content areas.

EA5. Use a standard dictionary to determine the meaning of unknown words (e.g., idioms and words with multiple meanings).

EA6. Use decoding skills and knowledge of academic and social vocabulary to achieve independent reading.

EA7. Recognize idioms, analogies, and metaphors used in literature and texts in content areas.

EA8. Read aloud with appropriate pacing, intonation, and expression increasingly complex narrative and expository texts.

READING COMPREHENSION.....................................

Beginning

B8. Read simple text and orally respond to factual comprehension questions by using key words or phrases.

B9. Understand and follow simple multiple-step oral directions for classroom or work-related activities.

B10. Recognize categories of common informational materials (e.g., newspaper, brochure).

B11. Orally identify, using key words or phrases, the main ideas and some details of familiar texts.

B12. Point out text features, such as the title, table of contents, and chapter headings.

B13. Use pictures, lists, charts, and tables found in informational materials, newspapers, and magazines to identify the factual components of compare-and-contrast patterns.

B14. Orally identify examples of fact and opinion and cause and effect in simple texts.

Early Intermediate

EI9. Read and orally respond to simple literary texts and texts in content areas by using simple sentences to answer factual comprehension questions.

EI10. Identify and follow some multiple-step directions for using simple mechanical devices and filling out basic forms.

EI11. Identify and orally explain categories of familiar informational materials by using simple sentences.

EI12. Read text and orally identify the main ideas and details of informational materials, literary text, and text in content areas by using simple sentences.

EI13. Read and orally identify examples of fact and opinion and cause and effect in written texts by using simple sentences.

EI14. Orally identify the factual components of simple informational materials by using key words or phrases.

LITERARY RESPONSE AND ANALYSIS

Beginning

B19. Create pictures, lists, and charts to orally identify the characteristics of three different forms of literature: fiction, nonfiction, and poetry.

B20. Recite simple poems.

Early Intermediate

EI19. Distinguish orally the characteristics of different forms of fiction and poetry by using simple sentences.

WRITING STRATEGIES

Beginning

B1. Organize and record information from selected literature and content areas by displaying it on pictures, lists, charts, and tables.

B2. Create simple sentences or phrases with some assistance.

B3. Write a brief narrative by using a few simple sentences that include the setting and some details.

Intermediate

I9. Read literature and respond orally to it by answering in detailed sentences factual comprehension questions.

I10. Read text and use detailed sentences to explain orally the main ideas and details of informational text, literary text, and text in content areas.

I11. Understand and orally explain most multiple-step directions for using a simple mechanical device and filling out simple applications.

I12. Identify and use detailed sentences to explain orally the differences among some categories of informational materials.

I13. Understand and orally identify the features and elements of common consumer (e.g., warranties, contracts, manuals) and informational materials (e.g., magazines and books).

Early Advanced

EA9. Identify and explain the main ideas and critical details of informational materials, literary texts, and texts in content areas.

EA10. Identify and explain the differences between various categories of informational materials (e.g., textbooks, newspapers, instructional materials).

EA11. Analyze a variety of rhetorical styles found in consumer (e.g., warranties, contracts, manuals) and informational materials (e.g., newspapers, magazines, and textbooks).

Early Advanced

EA13. Describe orally the major characteristics of several forms of poetry by using detailed sentences.

EA18. Describe the major characteristics of several forms of fiction and poetry: short story, essay, novel, ballad, lyric, epic.

B4. Use the writing process to write brief narratives and stories with a few standard grammatical forms.

B5. Write simple compositions, such as descriptions and comparison and contrast, that have a main idea and some detail.

B6. Complete basic business forms in which information such as one's name, address, and telephone number is requested.

Early Intermediate

EI1. Write simple sentences of brief responses to selected literature to show factual understanding of the text.

EI2. Use common verbs, nouns, and high-frequency modifiers in writing simple sentences.

EI3. Create a draft of a paragraph by following an outline.

EI4. Write an increasing number of words and simple sentences appropriate for language arts and other content areas (e.g., math, science, history-social science).

EI5. Write expository compositions, such as descriptions, comparison and contrast, and problem and solution, that include a main idea and some details in simple sentences.

EI6. Collect information from various sources (e.g., dictionary, library books, research materials) and take notes on a given topic.

EI7. Proceed through the writing process to write short paragraphs that contain supporting details about a given topic. There may be some inconsistent use of standard grammatical forms.

EI8. Complete simple informational documents related to career development (e.g., bank forms and job applications).

Intermediate

I1. Narrate a sequence of events and communicate their significance to the audience.

I2. Write brief expository compositions (e.g., description, comparison and contrast, cause and effect, and problem and solution) that include a thesis and some points of support.

I3. Develop a clear purpose in a short essay by appropriately using the rhetorical devices of quotations and facts.

I4. Write responses to selected literature that exhibit understanding of the text, using detailed sentences and transitions.

I5. Use more complex vocabulary and sentences appropriate for language arts and other content areas (e.g., math, science, history-social science).

I6. Write documents related to career development (e.g., business letter, job application).

I7. Use complex sentences in writing brief fictional biographies and short stories that include a sequence of events and supporting details.

I8. Use basic strategies of notetaking, outlining, and the writing process to structure drafts of simple essays, with consistent use of standard grammatical forms (Some rules may not be followed.).

I9. Investigate and research a topic in a content area and develop a brief essay or report that includes source citations.

Early Advanced

EA1. Write in different genres (e.g., short stories and narratives), including coherent plot development, characterization, and setting.

EA2. Develop a clear thesis and support it by using analogies, quotations, and facts appropriately.

EA3. Write responses to selected literature that develop interpretations, exhibit careful reading, and cite specific parts of the text.

EA4. Use appropriate language variations and genres in writing for language arts and other content areas.

EA5. Write pieces related to career development (e.g., business letter, job application, letter of inquiry).

EA6. Write persuasive and expository compositions that include a clear thesis, describe organized points of support, and address a counterargument.

EA7. Write detailed fictional biographies or autobiographies.

EA8. Use strategies of notetaking, outlining, and summarizing to structure drafts of clear, coherent, and focused essays with consistent use of standard grammatical forms.

EA9. Write an essay or report that balances information, has original ideas, and gives credit to sources in a bibliography. Use appropriate tone and voice for the purpose, audience, and subject matter.

LISTENING AND SPEAKING STRATEGIES AND APPLICATIONS . . . .

B1. Begin to speak a few words or sentences by using some English phonemes and rudimentary English grammatical forms (e.g., single words or phrases).

B2. Ask and answer questions by using simple sentences or phrases.

B3. Demonstrate comprehension of oral presentations and instructions through nonverbal responses (e.g., gestures, pointing, drawing).

B4. Independently use common social greetings and simple repetitive phrases (e.g., "Good morning, Ms. ____").

Early Intermediate

EI1. Begin to be understood when speaking but may have some inconsistent use of standard English grammatical forms and sounds (e.g., plurals, simple past tense, pronouns such as he or she).

EI2. Ask and answer questions by using phrases or simple sentences.

EI3. Restate and execute multiple-step oral directions.

EI4. Restate in simple sentences the main idea of oral presentations in subject-matter content.

EI5. Orally communicate basic needs (e.g., "I need to borrow a pencil").

Intermediate

I1. Respond to messages by asking simple questions or by briefly restating the message.

I2. Listen attentively to stories and information and identify important details and concepts by using both verbal and nonverbal responses.

I3. Make oneself understood when speaking by using consistent standard English grammatical forms and sounds; however, some rules may not be followed (e.g., third-person singular, male and female pronouns).

I4. Participate in social conversations with peers and adults on familiar topics by asking and answering questions and soliciting information.

I5. Identify the main idea and some supporting details of oral presentations, familiar literature, and key concepts of subject-matter content.

I6. Prepare and deliver short presentations on ideas, premises, or images obtained from various common sources.

Early Advanced

EA1. Listen attentively to more complex stories and information on new topics across content areas and identify the main points and supporting details.

EA2. Retell stories in greater detail by including the characters, setting, and plot.

EA3. Make oneself understood when speaking by using consistent standard English grammatical forms, sounds, intonation, pitch, and modulation but may make random errors.

EA4. Participate in and initiate more extended social conversations with peers and adults on unfamiliar topics by asking and answering questions and restating and soliciting information.

EA5. Recognize appropriate ways of speaking that vary according to the purpose, audience, and subject matter.

EA6. Respond to messages by asking questions, challenging statements, or offering examples that affirm the message.

EA7. Use simple figurative language and idiomatic expressions (e.g., "heavy as a ton of bricks," "soaking wet") to communicate ideas to a variety of audiences.

EA8. Prepare and deliver presentations that use various sources.

SPEAKING APPLICATIONS . . . .

Early Intermediate

EI6. Prepare and deliver short oral presentations.

Intermediate

I6. Prepare and deliver short presentations on ideas, premises, or images obtained from various common sources.

Early Advanced

EA8. Prepare and deliver presentations that use various sources.

ENGLISH LANGUAGE CONVENTIONS . . . .

Beginning

B7. Edit one's own work and correct the punctuation.

B8. Identify basic vocabulary, mechanics, and sentence structures in a piece of writing.

B9. Revise one's writing for proper use of final punctuation, capitalization, and correct spelling.

Early Intermediate

EI9. Edit writing for basic conventions (e.g., punctuation, capitalization, and spelling).

EI10. Revise writing, with teacher's assistance, to clarify meaning and improve the mechanics and organization.

EI11. Use clauses, phrases, and mechanics of writing with consistent variations in grammatical forms.

Intermediate

I10. Revise writing for appropriate word choice and organization with variation in grammatical forms and spelling.

I11. Edit and correct basic grammatical structures and usage of the conventions of writing.

Early Advanced

EA10. Create coherent paragraphs through effective transitions.

EA11. Revise writing for appropriate word choice, organization, consistent point of view, and transitions, with some variation in grammatical forms and spelling.

EA12. Edit writing for grammatical structures and the mechanics of writing.

PICTURE IT!

A Comprehension Handbook

Author's Purpose

An author writes for many purposes, some of which are to inform, to entertain, to persuade, or to express. An author may have more than one purpose for writing.

Inform

Entertain

Persuade

Express

Cause and Effect

An effect is something that happens. A cause is why that thing happens. An effect sometimes has more than one cause. A cause sometimes has more than one effect. Clue words such as *because, as a result, therefore,* and *so that* can signal causes and effects.

Cause

Effect

Compare and Contrast

To compare and contrast is to look for similarities and differences in things. Clue words such as *like* or *as* show similarities. Clue words such as *but* or *unlike* show differences.

Context Clues

You can use context clues—the words and phrases around an unfamiliar word—to determine the meaning of an unfamiliar word.

Draw Conclusions

When we draw conclusions, we make sensible decisions or form reasonable opinions after thinking about the facts and details in what we are reading.

Fact and Opinion

A fact is something that can be proved. Facts are based on evidence.
Opinions express ideas and are based on interpretation of evidence.

Main Idea and Details

Main idea is the most important idea about a topic.

Details are smaller pieces of information that support the main idea.

Making Predictions

To make predictions, use text, graphics, and prior knowledge to predict what might happen in a story or what you might learn from a text. As you read, new information can lead to new or revised predictions.

Making Inferences

When we make inferences, or infer something, we come to a conclusion based on a detail an author provides in the text.

Paraphrasing

Paraphrasing is restating a sentence or an idea in your own words. Paraphrasing can lead to a better understanding of what we read.

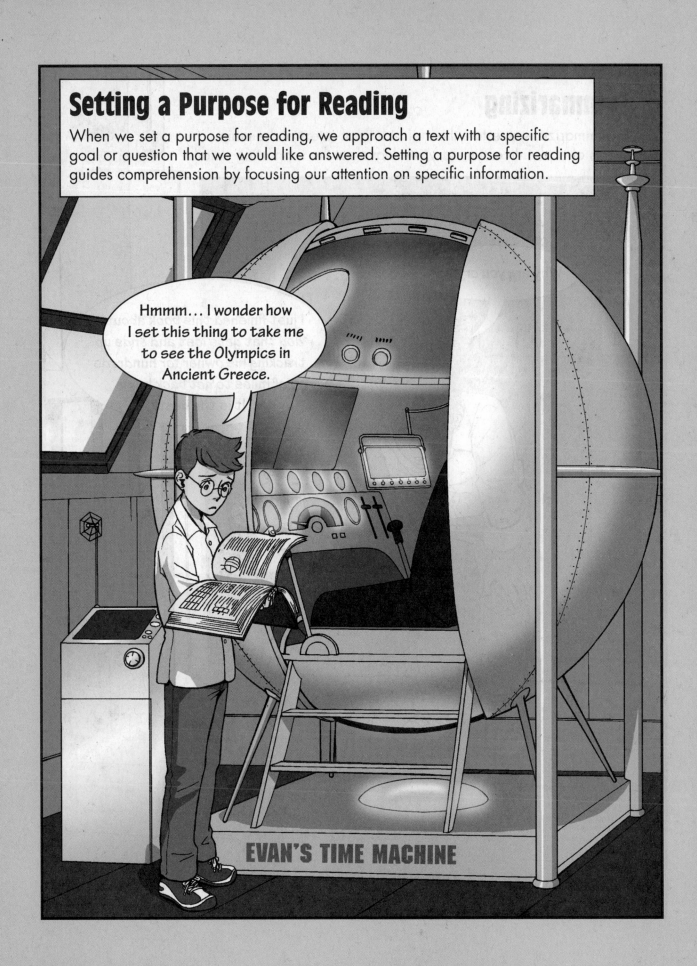

Setting a Purpose for Reading

When we set a purpose for reading, we approach a text with a specific goal or question that we would like answered. Setting a purpose for reading guides comprehension by focusing our attention on specific information.

Summarizing

To summarize, we restate the main ideas of a text or the main events of a plot. In a summary, we leave out the supporting details.

Why are you crying?

I just finished this book about a dog that gets lost and ends up tracking his owner for hundreds of miles to get back home. It is the best!

How do we decide what is true?

In this unit, I will read:

In this unit, I will:

- learn new vocabulary words.
- read about different topics.
- use my background knowledge.
- use details to revise predictions.
- use fact and opinion words.
- confirm facts and opinions.
- make and support predictions.
- know the difference between facts and opinions.
- learn about common and proper nouns.

- learn about singular and plural nouns.
- learn about personal and possessive pronouns.
- learn about interrogative and indefinite pronouns.
- write predictions.
- write to confirm predictions.
- write facts and opinions.
- write sentences to confirm facts.

How do we decide what is true?

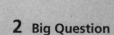

Connect to the Big Question

Answer these questions.
Discuss your answers with your teacher and classmates.

How do you decide what is true?
What does the truth mean to you?

Extend the Big Question

Read each sentence frame. Write your opinions in each blank.

Sometimes you can find the truth by _____

_____

_____

_____

_____

Sometimes the truth is difficult to find because _____

_____

_____

_____

_____

_____.

Discuss your opinions with your teacher and classmates.

ELA LS 1.4 Select a focus, an organizational structure, and a point of view, matching the purpose, message, occasion, and vocal modulation to the audience. ELA LS 1.7 Use effective rate, volume, pitch, and tone and align nonverbal elements to sustain audience interest and attention. (ELD LS B1, B2, B3, EI1, EI2, EI3, I1, I2, I3, I4, EA1, EA2, EA3, EA4, EA5, EA6)

Vocabulary Workshop

Answer the Questions Read each question. Choose
a word from the Big Question Words list to answer each
question. Write your answer on the line.

1. What does a police officer look for at a crime scene?

_____

2. What word describes something that is real?

_____

3. What word means the opposite of "false"?

_____

4. What would you do to get ready
for a test?

_____

5. What word describes a
belief you have?

_____

Big Question Words

Use your definitions from
page 21 of the *Review
and Assess* book.

confirm
(cognate: confirmar)

decision
(cognate: decisión)

determine
(cognate: determinar)

evidence
(cognate: evidencia)

fact

fantasy
(cognate: fantasia)

fiction
(cognate: ficción)

investigate
(cognate: investigar)

opinion
(cognate: opinión)

prove
(cognate: comprobar)

realistic
(cognate: realista)

study
(cognate: estudiar)

test

true

unbelievable

Use Context Fill in the lines with Big Question Words.

You need to use your head to make a good

___decision___ . For example, Ranita is voting for Julia

for class president because Julia is pretty. I told Ranita

she cannot ___determine___ the best person for the job

by the way someone looks. She must ___prove___

that Julia should be president. I told her to look for a

___fact___ . For example, Julia is a good leader.

Once she can ___confirm___ that about Julia, then

Ranita will know Julia is the right person for the job.

 ELA V 1.4 Monitor expository text for unknown words or words with novel meanings by using word,
sentence, and paragraph clues to determine meaning. **ELA V 1.5** Understand and explain "shades of
meaning" in related words. **(ELD V B1, B2, EI1, EI2, EI3, I1, I2, EA1, EA2)**

Roots A word's root can give you clues about the meaning of a word. A root is the basic part of a word. It usually contains a word's basic meaning. Roots come from many different languages, including Greek and Latin. The Spanish language also shares some common roots with English. Prefixes and suffixes can be added to a root to change its meaning.

Here are some common roots you might find in some words:

- The Latin root -*dict*- means "to say or tell." You can find this root in words like *dictate* and *dictation*.
- The Latin root -*ver*- means "truth." You can find this root in words like *verify* and *veracity*.

. . . .

Find the Root Circle the root in each of the following words. Write each word's definition. If you need help, use a dictionary. Most dictionaries can tell you the root or roots of a word.

edict: _____

support: _____

hydrate: _____

observe: _____

dental: _____

verity: _____

. . . .

Word Origins Sometimes, knowing a word's origin can help you understand unfamiliar words. Many words in English come from different places and languages.

For example, you can use a dictionary to look up the origin of the word *fantasy.* That word comes from the Greek word *phantasia,* which means "appearance". Also, if you know Spanish, the Greek word *phantasia* looks like the Spanish word *fantasía.*

Find the Origin Choose three Big Question Words from page 4. Write the words in the space below. Then, use a dictionary to find the word's origin. Write the word's origin next to the word.

Word: _____   Origin: _____

Word: _____   Origin: _____

Word: _____   Origin: _____

ELA V 1.3 Recognize the origins and meanings of frequently used foreign words in English and use these words accurately in speaking and writing. **(ELD V B7, EI4, I3, I4, EA3, EA5)**

Vocabulary Workshop 5

THE BIG ?

Lesson 1
How do we decide
what is true?

Vocabulary

Important Words

decision: a choice about something (cognate: decisión)

facts: something that is true; pieces of information that can be proven

opinion: a belief based on facts and experience (cognate: opinión)

unbelievable: unlikely to be true; impossible

Concept Words

admission: the right to enter somewhere (cognate: admisión)

shelter: a safe place, like a home

unwanted: not wanted; not welcome

Animal Shelters

Dialogue

These two teenagers are talking about homeless animals. Read the dialogue. Think about what the teenagers are talking about. Then, review the vocabulary words you read.

Teenager 1: I found this old lost dog. I'm thinking about taking him to an animal shelter.

Teenager 2: You should take him to a "no-kill" shelter so he has a better chance of being adopted.

Teenager 1: Why not the "open-admission" shelter down the street?

Teenager 2: They will euthanize, or kill the dog after a set number of days.

Teenager 1: That's unbelievable! I can't believe they kill animals.

Teenager 2: There are a lot of unwanted animals in the world. The "open-admission" shelter has to make room, but the animals are not hurt when they die.

Teenager 1: My opinion is that this dog deserves a chance.

Teenager 2: It's good you've listened to all the facts. I'm sure the dog will agree with your decision.

Talk About It Discuss the question with a partner or in a small group. Have you ever been to an animal shelter? Would you take a homeless animal to one? If not, where would you take it? Complete the sentence frame.

If I found a lost animal I would take it to no-kill shelter

because that diserve to live

Reading

Read the article. As you read, think about these questions:
- How would you decide where to take a lost animal?
- How does the topic of the article relate to the topic of the dialogue?

Shelters work hard to find homes for animals.

A Place Where Strays Can Stay

Where do unwanted dogs or cats go? Every year, millions of dogs and cats are taken to animal shelters. What happens at the shelter? That depends on what kind it is.

"Open-admission" shelters will care for any animal for a set number of days. If the animal has not been adopted within that time, it is euthanized. Euthanize means that the animal is put to death. Killing animals may seem unbelievable, but the shelters must make space for new animals. The euthanized animals feel no pain.

Another type of shelter is called "no-kill." Animals stay in these shelters until they are adopted, and are never euthanized unless they are very sick or dangerous. This can mean that some animals spend their whole lives in cages waiting to be adopted. It also means "no-kill" shelters are usually full.

Which kind of shelter would you put an animal in? It is a difficult decision. People should weigh the facts on both sides before forming an opinion.

Talk About It Work in groups of three or four. What are the good and bad things about each shelter? How would you decide where to take a lost animal? Complete the sentence frame.

To decide where to take a lost animal, I would ~~thak~~ he to a no-kill sheelt becuse they wont kill them if they dont adopt them

ELA V 1.4 Monitor expository text for unknown words or words with novel meanings by using word, sentence, and paragraph clues to determine meaning. (ELD V B1, EI1, I1, EA1) ELA R 2.3 Connect and clarify main ideas by identifying their relationships to other sources and related topics. (ELD R B8, EI9, I9, EA9)

FORM & FUNCTION

Important Words

background: a person's experience or knowledge; the culture and values with which a person has been raised

predict: to figure out or guess what might happen next (*cognate: predecir*)

Background Knowledge Background knowledge is something that you already know about the characters or story. Background knowledge can help you understand what you are reading and predict what might happen next.

For example, look at the sequence of events in the passage below:

> Hakim always dreamed of getting a black kitten with blue eyes. Finally, his birthday came and his parents took him to a shelter to pick out a kitten. There were white, brown, and orange kittens. A fluffy white kitten came up and rubbed Hakim's leg. It looked up with its big brown eyes. Hakim had to make a decision.

Story Clues

Hakim wants a black kitten.

Background Knowledge

All kittens are cute.

Prediction

Hakim will probably pick the white kitten instead.

Talk About It Discuss the questions with a partner or in a small group. What if Hakim saw a grown black cat at the shelter? Do you think he would have chosen it over the white kitten? Complete the sentence frame.

Hakim would have chosen the _____

because _____

_____.

Extend Language Use your background knowledge and the story clues to answer the following questions:

1. What do you already know about kittens? Kittens are _____

_____.

2. What might happen to the white kitten if Hakim does not adopt it? If Hakim does not adopt the kitten it might _____

_____.

3. How might Hakim feel when looking at the white kitten? Hakim probably feels _____

_____.

ELA R 2.4 Clarify an understanding of texts by creating outlines, logical notes, summaries, or reports. **(ELD R B8, EI9, I9, EA9)**

Comprehension Workshop

FORM & FUNCTION

Make Predictions You can organize information to help you predict what is going to happen next in a story. Charts can help you organize what you are thinking. Read the story. Then, use your background knowledge and story clues to make a prediction in the chart below.

Maria loves animals, especially puppies and kittens. One day, she came across an old lost dog. The dog was unwanted and alone. She already had too many pets, so she took it to a "no-kill" shelter, but it was full. Maria then took it to an "open-admission" shelter and was told they would keep it for a month. After that, it would be euthanized. Maria weighed the facts and decided what to do.

Older animals might stay in no-kill shelters all their lives.

Background Knowledge	Details from Story	Prediction

If you need help, think about these questions:

- Background knowledge: What do you know about lost animals?
- Details from story: What do you know about how Maria feels about animals?
- Prediction: What do you think Maria will do?

. . . .

Extend Comprehension Complete the chart to show how you used details from the story to make predictions about what Maria might do. Follow the example in the chart below.

Details from Story	Prediction
She already had too many pets.	She might try to put the dog in a shelter.

ELA R 2.4 Clarify an understanding of texts by creating outlines, logical notes, summaries, or reports. **(ELD R B8, EI9, I9, EA9)**

Grammar

Important Words

common: ordinary, general; not specific; easy to find (*cognate: común*)

proper noun: a specific person, place, or thing (*cognate: propio*)

noun: a word that names a person, place, or thing (*cognate: nombre*)

Common and Proper Nouns A common noun names any person, place, or thing. Common nouns are never capitalized unless they begin a sentence. A proper noun names a specific person, place, or thing, and is always capitalized.

Here are some examples.

Common nouns	Proper nouns
girl	Maria
state	California

Extend Grammar Underline the common nouns and circle the proper nouns in each sentence.

1. Jackson feels protected by his dog, Chopper, because the dog barks at strangers.

2. Raphael thinks "no-kill" shelters are more humane.

The law

3. Animal shelters in California must follow strict laws.

The Kitten

4. Jennifer found a lost kitten next to Martha's Diner.

5. All shelters in Texas find homes for lost animals.

6. Linda thinks leaving animals in cages is cruel.

7. Javier says that animals that are euthanized in shelters are not hurt.

8. The dog ran up to Rachel and licked her face.

Adopting from an animal shelter helps save animals.

ELA LC 1.0 Students write and speak with a command of standard English conventions appropriate to the grade level. **LC 1.4** Use correct capitalization. **(ELD LC B8, EI9, I10, EA12)**

Connect to Writing

Write Predictions Think about all you have learned in this lesson. What new words did you use? What predictions did you make? Talk with a partner about what you learned.

Read the passage.

Last summer, my friends and I found a lost kitten. It was very small, dirty, and hungry. We knew that our parents would not let us keep it. I suggested we take it to a nearby "open-admission" shelter. My friend Maria was worried it would be euthanized. My friend Jackson didn't want the kitten locked in a cage. We argued all afternoon about what to do. It was getting late and we had to make a decision.

On a separate sheet of paper, write a prediction about each character. Use the sentence frames to answer the following question:

• Which kind of animal shelter would each person choose?

I think the narrator would choose an _Open admisson_ shelter because _It's very hungry and dirty_.

I think Maria would choose a _open mse_ shelter because _no one is going to take it_

I think Jackson _will not_ choose a shelter because _he don't want people locking them up in cages_

- -

Tell a Story Work with a partner. Tell a story about an animal character who is taken to a shelter. How does the animal feel? Who helps the animal? After you practice telling the story with your partner, share your story with other classmates.

Tips for Your Story

• Give names to your characters.

• Think of the story's problem and its solution.

• Use your voice correctly as you tell the story. Do your characters have different voices? How would you change your voice to explain this?

ELA LS 1.2 Identify the tone, mood, and emotion conveyed in the oral communication. **ELA LS 1.7** Use effective rate, volume, pitch, and tone and align nonverbal elements to sustain audience interest and attention. **ELA LS 2.1** Deliver narrative presentations. **ELA W 2.4** Write responses to literature. (**ELD LS B1, B2, EI1, I2, I3, EA1, EA2, EA3, EA5**)

Lesson 2
How do we decide what is true?

Vocabulary

Important Words

confirm: to check to make sure something is true *(cognate: confirmar)*

determine: to decide something *(cognate: determinar)*

intently: firmly; with a strong focus

opinion: a belief based on facts and experience *(cognate: opinión)*

realistic: real; life-like *(cognate: realista)*

Concept Words

allowance: money you might get for doing work at home

manage: to control something; to handle correctly *(cognate: manejar)*

responsible: behaving in a good way; following rules *(cognate: responsable)*

Parents and Allowances

Dialogue

Two teenagers are talking about saving and spending money. Read the dialogue. Then, review the vocabulary words you read.

> **Teenager 1:** I really want that new MP3 player. I'm saving my allowance to buy it. I should have enough saved to get it next month.

> **Teenager 2:** I want it too, but I can never save money. My dad says it confirms his theory that I'm not responsible enough.

> **Teenager 1:** You just have to learn to manage your money like me. I determine how much I need, then set it aside each month until I reach the goal.

> **Teenager 2:** That's not realistic for me. I always spend the money right away, and then wish I had it later. My dad is probably right about me.

> **Teenager 1:** Well that's his opinion. But I bet if you focused intently on saving, you could get the MP3 player, too.

Talk About It Discuss the question with a partner or in a small group. Which teenager is most like you? Use the sentence frame to explain why.

I am most like _tenager 2_

because _I like to speed my mony fast_

Reading

Read the article. As you read, think about these questions:
- How do kids learn about managing money?
- Do you agree with the evidence the author presents?

SMART MONEY

Clothes, music, cell phones: where do kids get money for the things they want? Some kids work odd jobs for money. Others get a regular **allowance**, and some have parents who buy the things they want. Usually parents **determine** how a kid learns to **manage** money.

Many people think that earning an allowance teaches kids how to be **responsible** with money. There are many different **opinions** about how to teach money management.

Some parents believe their children should do chores for money. But some kids refuse to help with anything unless they are paid. Others don't care about money and refuse to work **intently** at any job.

Where do kids get money for things they want?

Some parents believe that kids should do chores as part of life, not because they are getting paid. These parents might give their kids a set allowance that isn't tied to work. Some argue this model isn't **realistic** because the money isn't earned.

Whatever the method, studies **confirm** that kids who get an allowance learn how to make decisions about money.

Talk About It Discuss the questions with a partner or in a small group. Did you get an allowance? If you were a parent, which kind of allowance would you give your child? Why? Complete the sentence frame.

If I were a parent, I would _____

_____

because _____

_____

_____

ELA V 1.4 Monitor expository text for unknown words or words with novel meanings by using word, sentence, and paragraph clues to determine meaning. **(ELD V B1, EI1, I1, EA1) ELA R 2.6** Determine the adequacy and appropriateness of the evidence for an author's conclusions. **(ELD R B8, EI9, I9, EA9)**

Language Workshop

FORM & FUNCTION

Important Words

confirm: to check to make sure something is true *(cognate: confirmar)*

details: a piece of information *(cognate: detalle)*

revise: to look again and correct *(cognate: revisar)*

Details and Predictions Details are clues and information found in the story.

Read the story below. Use details from the story to make predictions about what will happen next. Then read ahead to find more details that confirm whether or not your prediction was correct. If necessary, revise your prediction.

Tom and I went to the corner store to buy groceries for my mom. Tom kept looking over his shoulder. He was nervous about running into Lily, a girl from school. As we rounded a corner, we heard a girl's voice call out to us. Tom spun around.

Story Detail

The boys hear a voice.

Prediction

The voice is probably coming from Lily, a girl from Tom's school.

Background Knowledge

I can recognize voices.

Talk About It Why do you think Tom thought it was Lily's voice? Discuss the question with a partner or in a small group. Then, complete the sentence frame.

Tom thought it was Lily's voice because ___Tome like lily and he was nerveuse___

Now read ahead:

Standing behind us was my sister, Dahlia. She was holding a loaded squirt gun, pointed straight at us. "Don't you dare!" I said, just as she started laughing louder.

Extend Language What new details did you find when reading ahead? Use the new details to verify or revise your prediction.

☑ My prediction was correct.

☐ My prediction was incorrect and needs to be revised.

New Detail

I's tom's sister who is Dahlia.

New Prediction

I Think Dahlia is going to squirt him

ELA R 2.4 Clarify an understanding of texts by creating outlines, logical notes, summaries, or reports. (ELD R B8, EI9, I9, EA9)

Comprehension Workshop ⓢ FORM & FUNCTION

Make Predictions A prediction is stronger when you use background knowledge and details from the story. Read the article. Use the chart below to help organize your thoughts. As you read, think about these questions:

- What background knowledge do you have about getting and saving money?

- How does each character manage their money?

How do teenagers learn to be responsible with money?

 Max and Lola went to the mall. Max had just gotten his allowance and couldn't wait to spend it. Lola didn't get an allowance. She babysat and mowed lawns for money. She had some money saved, but wasn't planning on spending it today. First, Max bought candy for them to share. Then, he played some video games. Then, he bought a new sweatshirt and some jeans. Soon, his money was running out and he asked Lola, "Can I borrow some money?"

What I Know About Getting and Saving Money	What I Know About Lola	My Prediction About Lola's Answer
I just get money and work for money	Lola wants to save her money	Lola is going to say no

Extend Comprehension Now read ahead. As you read, think about the new details you are learning. Use the new details to verify or revise your prediction.

 Lola said, "No, I'm saving my money." Max frowned and said, "Why do you have to be so responsible?" She replied, "Because I work hard for it." Just then, they passed a shop with Lola's favorite ice cream. She turned to Max and smiled.

☑ My prediction was correct.

☐ My prediction was incorrect and needs to be revised.

→ **New Detail**
they passed lolas favorite ice cream shop

→ **New Prediction**
lola is going to buy her ice cream

ELA R 2.4 Clarify an understanding of texts by creating outlines, logical notes, summaries, or reports. **(ELD R B8, EI9, I9, EA9)**

Grammar

Important Words

plural: more than one (cognate: *plural*)

singular: one thing; not plural (cognate: *singular*)

Singular and Plural Nouns A singular noun is one person, place, or thing. A plural noun is more than one. Although some nouns form plurals differently, adding the letter -*s* or the letters -*es* to the end of the word usually forms a plural noun. Remember that adding -*es* to a word also adds a syllable.

Singular nouns	decision, kid, allowance, job, bus
Plural nouns	decisions, kids, allowances, jobs, buses

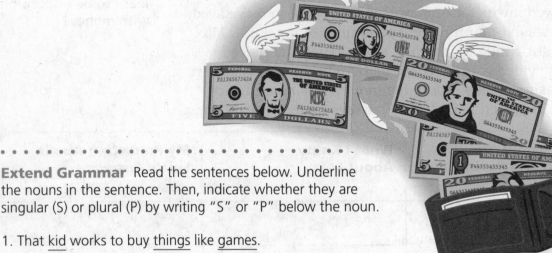

Extend Grammar Read the sentences below. Underline the nouns in the sentence. Then, indicate whether they are singular (S) or plural (P) by writing "S" or "P" below the noun.

1. That <u>kid</u> works to buy <u>things</u> like <u>games</u>.
     S   P   P

2. Some kids have odd jobs.

3. My friend gets an allowance from his parents.

4. There are many different opinions about this subject.

5. Many grandparents believe kids should do chores.

6. My brother might do a job for free.

7. My sister gets an allowance, but I do not.

8. Some teachers talk to students about allowances.

9. Some kids put their money in a bank.

10. My dad leaves me two dollars every morning for my allowance.

Some people can't seem to hold on to their money.

ELA LC 1.0 Students write and speak with a command of standard English conventions appropriate to the grade level. (ELD LC B8, EI9, I10, EA12)

Connect to Writing

Writing Tips

Don't forget to

1. use your background knowledge about getting and managing money.

2. use details to form predictions.

3. go back and revise your writing.

Write to Confirm Predictions How did you use background knowledge and details to form predictions? Talk with a partner about what you learned.

The characters below are going to the mall together. Read about each character. Use your background knowledge and details from the article, "Smart Money," to form predictions.

Matt: His parents give him an allowance for doing chores around the house. He only works if he gets paid.

Elijah: His parents pay for everything he wants. He always gets the popular things before Matt and Juanita.

Juanita: Her parents expect her to do chores without pay, but give her spending money. She thinks Matt and Elijah are lazy.

On a separate piece of paper, write a paragraph answering the question: How will the characters manage their money at the mall?

If you need help, use these sentence frames:

At the mall, I think Matt will _____.

Elijah will probably _____,

and Juanita will _____.

Have a Dialogue Review the article about allowances. Work with a partner. Create a dialogue between two kids that talks about the main ideas in the article. What will the kids say? How do they feel about allowances?

Tips for Your Dialogue

• Think of what the two kids would say about allowances.

• Use your voice to express different emotions.

• Pay attention to how your partner is speaking. Is your partner using gestures? What do these gestures mean?

 ELA LS 1.1 Relate the speaker's verbal communication to the nonverbal message. **ELA LS 2.3** Deliver oral responses to literature. **(ELD B1, B2, B3, EI1, E12, I1, I3, I4, EA3, EA5)**

Lesson 3
How do we decide
what is true?

Vocabulary

Important Words

consequence: something that follows as a result of something else *(cognate: consecuencia)*

determine: to decide something *(cognate: determinar)*

prove: to show that something is true *(cognate: comprobar)*

true: right and accurate; able to be proven; the opposite of false

unbelievable: unlikely to be true; impossible

Concept Words

collide: when two things fight or cause problems

press: organizations such as newspapers, TV news channels, and news radio stations *(cognate: prensa)*

privacy: time or space to be left alone; opposite of public *(cognate: privacidad)*

Celebrity Privacy

Dialogue

These two students are talking about how celebrities are treated by the press. Read the dialogue. Then, review the vocabulary words you read.

Student 1: She looks terrible in a bathing suit! This article says she gained 50 pounds.

Student 2: Whether or not that's true, I feel sorry for her. She has a right to privacy. She's just trying to have a vacation!

Student 1: Look at this. It says she fought with her boyfriend the entire time!

Student 2: The press is out of hand. Don't you think stories like that have bad consequences for celebrities?

Student 1: Well fans have a right to know the real story.

Student 2: But how do you determine what is true? Can you prove that the facts are correct?

Student 1: Look at the picture. They are obviously fighting! This is unbelievable. Their car collided with a bus!

Student 2: Unbelievable is right. But it is the press that has collided with a celebrity's right to privacy.

Talk About It Discuss the questions with a partner or in a small group. Do you like reading about the private lives of celebrities? Why or why not? Then, complete the sentence frame.

I _____ reading about the private lives of

celebrities because _____

_____

_____

Reading

Read the article. As you read, think about these questions:
- Do celebrities have a right to privacy?
- How does the topic of the article relate to the topic of the dialogue?

celebrity scoop

Everyone wants to know more about their favorite actor, singer, or athlete. You can always find information about them in newspapers, magazines, the Internet, or on TV. But how do we determine if the information is true? Do we have the right to know about the private lives of celebrities?

All citizens in the United States have the right to privacy. This means you have the right to be left alone in your private life. Although celebrities depend on media attention for their fame, it can be a problem when they just want to walk the dog in peace.

Media organizations argue that viewers have a "right to know." Sometimes members of the press do unbelievable things to get a celebrity scoop, including following celebrities on their vacations or to their homes. The freedom of the press is legally protected, and sometimes there are consequences for celebrities. Sometimes they must prove that a media story is not true. This is where freedom of the press and the right to privacy collide.

Celebrities have very little privacy.

Talk About It Work with a partner or in a small group. Do you think celebrities have the right to privacy? Why or why not? Circle your opinion. Then, complete the sentence frame.

I think celebrities (do/do not) have the right to privacy because

_____

_____

_____

_____

ELA V 1.1 Read aloud narrative and expository text fluently and accurately and with appropriate pacing, intonation, and expression. (ELD V B1, EI1, I1, EA1, EA8) ELA R 2.3 Connect and clarify main ideas by identifying their relationships to other sources and related topics. (ELD V B8, EI9, I9, EA9)

Important Words

facts: pieces of information that can be proven true

opinion: a belief based on facts and experience *(cognate: opinión)*

Fact Words vs. Opinion Words Facts are details that can be proven. An opinion is a person's judgment or belief. As you read texts that contain many details, it is important to distinguish between facts and opinions.

Facts	Opinions	Judgments
Specific details that can be verified by a reference.	Statements that reflect a person's beliefs, such as *I believe.*	Statements that evaluate or offer an opinion such as *ugly, always, or best of all.*

Read the sentence. Underline the fact. Then, circle words that indicate opinions or judgments.

The freedom of the press is legally protected in the United States, but I believe news coverage of celebrities should be banned.

Talk About It Work with a partner or in a small group. Give some examples of the press going too far. Complete the following sentence frame.

I think the press goes too far when it _____

_____

_____

_____

Extend Language Read the chart. Then, decide if the sentence is a fact or an opinion.

Sentence	Fact	Opinion
1. All movie stars love media attention.		
2. Sports stars only care about money.		
3. Famous actors always dress nicely.		
4. That movie star won 17 awards.		
5. He lives at 1721 Broadway Boulevard.		

ELA R 2.4 Clarify an understanding of texts by creating outlines, logical notes, summaries, or reports. (ELD R B14, E113, I10, EA9)

Comprehension Workshop

Fact and Opinion Once you can tell the difference between facts and opinions, you may choose to verify facts yourself, or decide whether or not you agree with an author's opinion.

Go back to the article, "Celebrity Scoop." Write three facts from the article. Then, write two opinions. Does the author support his opinions?

Facts	Opinions
1. _____	1. _____
2. _____	2. _____
3. _____	

Freedom of the press is protected by law.

Extend Comprehension Think about your favorite singer, movie star, or athlete. Write one fact and one opinion about that person. Try to use new vocabulary. Use the sentence frames.

My favorite celebrity is _____.

One fact about _____

is _____

_____.

In my opinion, _____

is _____

_____.

ELA R 2.6 Determine the adequacy and appropriateness of the evidence for an author's conclusion. **(ELD R B14, E113, I10, EA9)**

Grammar

Important Words

personal: related to a person (cognate: personal)

possessive: showing ownership (cognate: posesivo)

pronoun: a word that replaces a noun (cognate: pronombre)

Personal and Possessive Pronouns A pronoun is a word that takes the place of a person or thing in a sentence. A personal pronoun usually refers to a person that appears elsewhere in the sentence or paragraph. It answers the question who? A possessive pronoun refers to something you may own. It answers the question whose is this?

Personal pronouns	Possessive pronouns
I, he, she, him, her, you, they, them, it	my, his, her, yours, their, its, our
I took a picture of the movie star. *She* winked at *me*.	The movie star gave me *her* autograph.

Extend Grammar Circle the pronoun in each sentence below. Then, decide if the pronoun is personal or possessive.

Sentence	Personal	Possessive
1. The right to privacy means the government can't tell people what to do in their private lives.		
2. The movie star waved her hand.		
3. Parents determine how to raise their kids.		
4. Reporters are scary. They bother stars.		
5. A newspaper must protect its sources.		
6. Politicians get more votes when they meet people in person.		
7. That movie star might like going to parties with her fans.		
8. We often like to hear gossip about celebrities.		

ELA LC 1.0 Students write and speak with a command of standard English conventions appropriate to the grade level. **(ELD LC B8, EI9, I10, EA12)**

Connect to Writing

Write Facts and Opinions Think of all you learned in this lesson. What new words did you use? How did you learn to tell the difference between facts and opinions? Discuss with a partner.

On a separate sheet of paper, write two paragraphs about celebrities. Answer the following questions:

- How can you identify a fact about a celebrity? Give an example.
- How can you identify an opinion about a celebrity? Give an example.

If you need help, use the sentence frames:

A fact about a celebrity is something that can be _____
_____.

For example, _____.

An opinion about a celebrity uses words like _____.

For example, _____.

Writing Tips
Don't forget to

1. remember how to identify facts.

2. think of language that signals opinions or judgments.

3. go back and revise your writing.

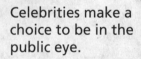

Write a Story On a separate sheet of paper, write a story about a celebrity character. You can create any character you like. What problem does the celebrity character have? What do other characters do in the story?

Use this chart to help organize your ideas.

My Story: _____

Character's Name: _____

Character's Problem: _____

What Other Characters Do: _____

Celebrities make a choice to be in the public eye.

Tips for Your Story

- Give names to your characters. Include a setting for your story.
- Include details and events. Make sure events are in the right order.
- Use the Writing Process Handbook at the end of this book. This will show you how to draft your story. It will also show you how to revise your story.

ELA W 1.6 Revise writing to improve the organization and consistency of ideas within and between paragraphs.
ELA W 2.1 Write narratives. (ELD B1, B2, B3, B4, EI2, EI4, I1, EA1 EA4)

THE BIG ?

Lesson 4
How do we decide
what is true?

Vocabulary

Important Words

evidence: a detail that shows that something is true (*cognate: evidencia*)

quote: to report something someone says

realistic: real life like (*cognate: realista*)

study: to think, read, and learn about a subject (*cognate: estudiar*)

test: an exam you take to check understanding

Concept Words

fear: a feeling caused by a sense of danger

intense: very strong (*cognate: intenso*)

phobia: a specific kind of fear (*cognate: fobia*)

Fears

Dialogue

The teacher and students are talking about fears that people have. Read the dialogue. Then, review the vocabulary words you read.

Teacher:	Today we're talking about fear and phobias. Who can talk about a fear you have?
Student 1:	I am afraid of dogs. When I see a dog I feel an intense panic, like I have to run away.
Teacher:	That may be evidence of a phobia, but you may outgrow it as you get older.
Student 2:	I am afraid of flying on airplanes, but I've done it twice.
Teacher:	The real test is whether your fear interrupts regular life. Some fear of flying is realistic. Since you overcame your fear, you probably don't have a phobia.
Student 3:	I had to study phobias for a class once. In the paper I wrote, I quoted a doctor who said that all phobias are really the fear of fear.
Teacher:	That's right.

Talk About It Discuss the question with a partner or in a small group. How is a phobia different from a regular fear? Then, complete the sentence frame.

A phobia is different from a regular fear because _____

_____

_____

_____

_____

Read the article. As you read, think about these questions:
- How is a phobia different from regular fear?
- How does the topic of the article relate to the topic of the dialogue?

THE FEAR FACTOR

Imagine being afraid of music or laughter! Some people are afraid of things that don't seem realistic to other people. If a fear is so intense that it interrupts your life, you may have a phobia. There are different types of phobias: social phobias, agoraphobia, and other specific phobias.

Most people feel nervous or shy in social situations like meeting someone new or taking a test. Social phobias go beyond normal fear, causing people to avoid situations that involve interacting with other people.

Agoraphobia is the fear of being in any situation that will cause a panic attack. Agoraphobic people often avoid leaving home at all!

Other specific phobias are fears about one thing. For example, scientists who study phobias once found a woman who was quoted as being so afraid of spiders that she wouldn't go out at night.

But if some fear is normal, how do you tell if you have a phobia? Irrational panic and terror are evidence of a phobia. All phobias are basically the fear of fear.

Talk About It Discuss the question with a partner or in a small group. Everyone is afraid of something. What are you afraid of? Then, complete the sentence frame.

I am afraid of _____.

I think it _____ a phobia because _____

_____

_____

_____

ELA V 1.4 Monitor expository text for unknown words or words with novel meanings by using word, sentence, and paragraph clues to determine meaning. (ELD V B1, EI1, I1, EA1) ELA R 2.3 Connect and clarify main ideas by identifying their relationships to other sources and related topics. (ELD R B8, EI9, I9, EA9)

FORM & FUNCTION

Important Words

confirm: to check to make sure something is true (cognate: confirmar)

distinguish: to tell the difference between two things (cognate: distinguir)

resources: something that can be used for support or help (cognate: recursos)

Confirming Facts When deciding what is true, it is important to distinguish between facts and opinions. Review the language clues in the chart below.

Facts	Opinions	Judgments
Specific details that can be verified by a reference.	Statements that reflect a person's beliefs, such as *I believe*, or *in my opinion*.	Statements that evaluate or offer an opinion, such as *ugly, always, or best of all*.

Facts are details that you can confirm by checking resources such as dictionaries, encyclopedias, and reliable websites. These types of resources contain facts. Opinions express judgments that can be supported but not proven.

Talk About It Discuss the question with a partner or in a small group. Listening to different opinions can be a good thing. Whose opinions do you trust? Then, complete the sentence frame.

I trust _____ opinion because _____

_____

_____

_____

Extend Language Read the chart. Determine if the statement can be confirmed with a resource.

Samples	Can this be confirmed?	
1. The fear of music is called *melophobia*.	Yes	No
2. Fear of flying is not realistic.	Yes	No
3. Thousands of Americans suffer from social phobias.	Yes	No
4. The worst phobia is agoraphobia.	Yes	No

ELA R 2.1 Identify the structural features of popular media and use the features to obtain information. (ELD R B14, E113, I10, EA9)

Comprehension Workshop

Fact and Opinion Charts like the one below can help you keep track of facts found in your reading. Use the article "The Fear Factor." Find another fact in the article and try to verify it with a resource book or a reliable webpage.

- Remember to look for details that can be verified.
- Identify opinions with words that signal a judgment.

Fact	Resource	True	False
There are different types of phobias: social phobias, agoraphobia, and specific phobias.	Internet	X	

Evidence of a phobia includes feelings of panic and terror.

· ·

Extend Comprehension Now use a dictionary, encyclopedia, or reliable webpage to verify the links between phobia names and their meanings.

Phobia name:	Relates to:	True	False
1. somniphobia	Fear of sleeping	X	
2. melophobia	Fear of melons		
3. arithmophobia	Fear of numbers		
4. geliophobia	Fear of gelatin		

ELA R 2.3 Connect and clarify main ideas by identifying their relationships to other sources and related topics. **(ELD R B10, B14, EI13, I10, EA9, EA10)**

Comprehension Workshop **27**

Grammar

Important Words

indefinite: not specific (*cognate: indefinido*)

interrogative: describes a sentence that asks a question (*cognate: interrogativo*)

pronoun: a word that replaces a noun (*cognate: pronombre*)

Interrogative and Indefinite Pronouns Interrogative pronouns are used in questions about a noun or another pronoun. Indefinite pronouns can be plural or singular, depending on how they are used.

Interrogative pronouns	Indefinite pronouns
who, whom, whose, what, which	some, other, none

Look at the passage. Then, circle the interrogative or indefinite pronouns.

What are you afraid of? Some pretend they are afraid of nothing, while others are afraid of everything. Which type are you?

Extend Grammar Identify the type of pronoun in each sentence.

Sentence	Interrogative	Indefinite
1. Who do you know that is afraid of public speaking?		
2. Which phobia do you think is the worst?		
3. Whose phobia do you know about?		
4. None seem to think phobias are fun.		
5. Others make fun of people with phobias.		

Now write a sentence or question with each pronoun.

Who _____

Which _____

Whose _____

None _____

Others _____

ELA LC 1.2 Identify and properly use indefinite pronouns and present perfect, past perfect, and future perfect verb tenses; ensure that verbs agree with compound subjects. **(ELD LC B8, EI9, I10, EA12)**

Connect to Writing

Writing Tips
Don't forget to

1. use language that shows the difference between fact and opinion.

2. confirm your facts with reliable resources.

3. go back and revise your writing.

Write to Confirm Facts How did you learn to confirm facts? Talk with a partner about what you learned.

Using the article, "The Fear Factor," or a reliable resource, pick a phobia that is most interesting to you. On a separate sheet of paper, write the answers to the following questions:

• What phobia is most interesting to you? Why? Write at least one fact and one opinion about the phobia.

If you need help, use these sentence frames.

> The phobia most interesting to me is _____.
>
> It is the fear of _____.
>
> One fact about this phobia is _____
>
> _____.
>
> I think _____
>
> _____.

Some people have a phobia of small spaces.

Connect to the Big Question Think about all the articles you read in this unit. What article did you like best? What article did you not like? Then, talk about your favorite article and say what the article was about.

Now, take some time to share your final ideas. Answer this question: How do we decide what is true? You can complete the sentence frame below. If you like, you can also choose another way to answer the question. Here are some choices: write a brief poem, a song, or a short paragraph.

> We decide what is true by _____
>
> _____
>
> _____

ELA W 1.1 Choose the form of writing that best suits the intended purpose. **LS 2.3** Deliver oral responses to literature. **(ELD W B2, EI1, I3, I4, EA2, EA3; LS B1, B2, EI1, EI2, I3, I4, EA4, EA5)**

Connect to Writing **29**

Vocabulary Review

Big Question Words and Important Words

confirm

consequence

decision

determine

evidence

fact

fantasy

fiction

intently

investigate

opinion

prove

quote

realistic

study

test

true

unbelievable

Best Definition Read the sentence. Circle the letter of the best definition for each underlined word.

1. My opinion is that animal shelters provide a good service.
   A. a belief
   B. a concern
   C. an investigation
   D. a true statement

2. We carefully gathered evidence.
   A. an opinion or common idea
   B. a detail that proves something
   C. an investigation
   D. a true statement

3. The doctor determined that Maria had a phobia.
   A. guessed
   B. argued
   C. studied
   D. decided

4. The story about the celebrity was realistic.
   A. describes something that is imagined
   B. describes something that has been tested
   C. describes something that is real
   D. describes something that is popular

Personal Response Circle the Big Question or Important Word in the sentence frame. Then, finish the sentence.

1. I recently made the decision to

_____.

2. My favorite subject to study is

_____.

3. The last test I took was

_____.

4. I can tell truth from fiction by

_____.

ELA V 1.4 Monitor expository text for unknown words or words with novel meanings by using word, sentence, and paragraph clues to determine meaning. **ELA V 1.5** Understand and explain "shades of meaning" in related words. **(ELD V B1, B2, EI1, EI2, EI3, I1, I2, EA1, EA2)**

Comprehension Review

Make Predictions Read the passage. Use your background knowledge and story clues, or details, to make a prediction about what will happen next. Then, fill in the diagram.

Important Words

- background
- confirm
- details
- predict
- revise

Olivia looked out the window at the dark night. Her heart began to pound. All she could imagine were the unseen spiders crawling through the grass and across the sidewalk. She saw the taxi pull up in front. The driver impatiently honked his horn.

Details	Background Knowledge	Prediction
_____	_____	_____
_____	_____	_____
_____	_____	_____
_____	_____	_____
_____	_____	_____
_____	_____	_____

- -

Change the Scene Reread the passage above. Now imagine that the same scene happened during the day. Revise the prediction. Complete the sentence frames.

1. I already know that Olivia _____

_____.

2. The clues in the story tell me _____

_____.

3. If it was daytime, I predict Olivia would _____

_____.

How do fears impact people?

ELA R 2.4 Clarify an understanding of texts by creating outlines, logical notes, summaries, or reports. **(ELD R B8, EI9, I9, EA9)**

Comprehension Review

Important Words
....
confirm

distinguish

fact

opinion

resources

Fact and Opinion A fact is a detail that can be proven. An opinion is a person's judgment or belief. Read the sentences. Then, circle either fact or opinion.

1. Fear of spiders is not realistic.

    fact   opinion

2. Thousands of Americans adopt animals from shelters.

    fact   opinion

3. He is terrible at managing his money.

    fact   opinion

4. I believe the celebrity meant what she said.

    fact   opinion

5. Somniphobia is the fear of sleeping.

    fact   opinion

. . . .

Confirm Facts Facts or details can be confirmed by using resources such as a dictionary, encyclopedia, atlas, map, or a reliable webpage. Read each fact below. Then, write the resource you would use to confirm it.

1. The animal shelter is located at 345 Main Street.

    _____.

2. A phobia is an unrealistic fear of something.

    _____.

3. Los Angeles is located at 34°N, 118°W.

    _____.

4. That celebrity was born August 31, 1955.

    _____.

5. The correct spelling of the word *prove* is p-r-o-v-e.

    _____.

Resources help confirm facts.

ELA R 2.3 Connect and clarify main ideas by identifying their relationships to other sources and related topics. **(ELD R B14, E113, I10, EA9)**

Complete the Sentence Choose the correct word to complete the sentence. Write the word on the line.

1. Someone found a lost pet next to _____ Diner. (Martha's/martha's)

2. Some _____ save their money in piggy banks. (kids/kid)

3. We often like to know things about _____ favorite movie stars. (my/our)

4. _____ bother me with their constant noise. (They/He)

5. _____ do you know that is afraid of the dark? (Who/Which)

Some teens get an allowance, while others work for money.

Replace the Word Replace the underlined word or words with the word in parentheses. Then, rewrite the sentences. Remember: other words in the new sentence may change as well.

1. <u>Some</u> of my friends are afraid of spiders. (which)

_____

_____

2. I don't get an allowance, but my <u>dad</u> leaves me some money in the morning. (parents)

_____

_____

3. <u>The movie star</u> took some photos with her fans. (She)

_____

_____

ELA LC 1.0 Students write and speak with a command of standard English conventions appropriate to the grade level. **(ELD LC B8, EI9, I10, EA12)**

Grammar Review **33**

How do we decide what is true?

In this unit, I read:

In this unit, I:

- learned new vocabulary words.
- read about different topics.
- used my background knowledge.
- used details to revise predictions.
- used fact and opinion words.
- confirmed facts and opinions.
- made and supported predictions.
- knew the difference between facts and opinions.
- learned about common and proper nouns.

- learned about singular and plural nouns.
- learned about personal and possessive pronouns.
- learned about interrogative and indefinite pronouns.
- wrote predictions.
- wrote to confirm predictions.
- wrote facts and opinions.
- wrote sentences to confirm facts.

Reflection Think about what you learned in this unit. Complete each sentence frame. Share your answers with your teacher and classmates.

I wonder _____.

I learned _____.

I discovered _____.

I still want to know _____.

I still don't understand _____.

 **Is conflict always bad?**

In this unit, I will read:

In this unit, I will:

- learn new vocabulary words.
- read about different topics.
- identify details.
- use my background knowledge.
- learn about questions.
- learn how to make inferences.
- learn how to draw conclusions.
- learn about verbs.

- learn about the principal parts of verbs.
- learn about simple verb tenses.
- learn about the perfect tenses of verbs.
- write sentences with details.
- write questions.
- write background knowledge paragraphs.

Is conflict always bad?

Connect to the Big Question
Answer these questions.
Discuss your answers with your teacher and classmates.

> How do you deal with conflict?
> When is conflict a good thing?

Extend the Big Question
Read each sentence frame.
Write your opinions in each blank.

I think conflicts are _____
_____
_____
_____
_____.

Conflicts can be
good if _____
_____
_____
_____
_____
_____.

Discuss your opinions with
your teacher and classmates.

 ELA LS 1.4 Select a focus, an organizational structure, and a point of view, matching the purpose, message, occasion, and vocal modulation to the audience. **ELA LS 1.7** Use effective rate, volume, pitch, and tone and align nonverbal elements to sustain audience interest and attention. **(ELD LS B1, B2, B3, EI1, EI2, EI3, I1, I2, I3, I4, EA1, EA2, EA3, EA4, EA5, EA6)**

Big Question Words

Use your definitions from page 21 of the *Review and Assess* book.

argue

battle
(cognate: batalla)

challenge

compete
(cognate: competir)

conclude
(cognate: concluir)

convince
(cognate: convencer)

defend
(cognate: defender)

game

issue

lose

negotiate
(cognate: negociar)

resist
(cognate: resistir)

resolve
(cognate: resolver)

survival

win

Vocabulary Workshop

Answer the Questions Read each question. Choose a word from the Big Question Words list to answer each question. Write your answer on the line.

1. Which word means almost the same as "to disagree"? _____

2. Which words means the opposite of something that is easy? _____

3. Which word means the same as "a struggle"? _____

4. Which word is the opposite of "lose"? _____

5. Which word means the same as "problem"? _____

Complete the Story Read the beginning of each story. Write the next sentence of the story. Use words from the list.

1. The baseball team had one goal today. The team wanted to win the game. It was going to be a challenge, but

_____

_____.

2. Juan had to do his homework, but he wanted to go to the game. He knew he had to negotiate with his mother.

_____

_____.

3. The coach had to conclude that it was okay to lose the game. He had to resist the feeling that winning is everything. He wanted to talk to his team. He told them

that _____

_____.

ELA V 1.4 Monitor expository text for unknown words or words with novel meanings by using word, sentence, and paragraph clues to determine meaning. **ELA V 1.5** Understand and explain "shades of meaning" in related words. **(ELD V B1, B2, EI1, EI2, EI3, I1, I2, EA1, EA2)**

Roots and Suffixes Roots and suffixes can give you clues about the meanings of words. A root is the basic part of a word. A suffix is an ending that you will find at the end of a word.

For example, the word *spectator* contains the root *spec* and the suffix *-or*. The root *spec* means "to look or watch." The suffix *-or* means "one who." So, *spectator* means "one who looks or watches."

Write Words Look at the roots and suffixes in the chart below. Write a word that contains the root or suffix. You can use a dictionary to help you.

Root	Meaning	Word
struct	to build	
port	carry	

Suffix	Meaning	Word
ful	full of	
hood	condition, quality	

Write Sentences Use four words from the chart to write four sentences. You can use a dictionary to help you with the meaning of the words.

ELA V 1.4 Monitor expository text for unknown words or words with novel meanings by using word, sentence, and paragraph clues to determine meaning. **(ELD V B1, B2, EI1, EI2, EI3, I1, I2, EA1, EA2)**

Lesson 1
Is conflict
always bad?

Vocabulary

Important Words

argue: to give reasons for or against an idea

compete: to make an effort to win *(cognate: competir)*

instructions: directions telling you what to do *(cognate: instrucciones)*

lose: fail to succeed; not win

negotiate: to agree with discussion and to compromise *(cognate: negociar)*

Concept Words

birth order: the order that children in a family are born

rivalry: a strong or intense competition *(cognate: rivalidad)*

sibling: a brother or sister

Sibling Rivalry

Dialogue

A research scientist and a student are talking about sibling rivalry. Read the dialogue. Then, review the vocabulary words you read.

Scientist: Hello, class, I am here to talk about links between birth order and personality. According to their birth order, children seem to get different instructions on how to act. Who here is a middle child?

Student: I am. I have an older brother and a younger sister.

Scientist: How do you get along with your siblings?

Student: My brother argues a lot, and my little sister is a pest. So I negotiate their fights.

Scientist: Many middle-born children negotiate rivalry between siblings. Why does your brother argue?

Student: He likes to compete.

Scientist: Many first-born children feel pressure to compete. How is your sister?

Student: My sister is the most competitive. She hates to lose and doesn't get along with anyone.

Scientist: That's strange. Usually the child born last gets along with others.

Talk About It Discuss the questions with a partner or in a small group. Do you have siblings? Are you an only child? Circle your opinon. Then, complete the sentence frame.

I am _____ in my family.

I (like/do not like) it because _____

_____

_____

_____

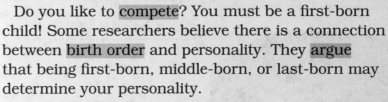

Reading

Read the article. As you read, think about these questions.

- How does birth order affect personality?
- How does the topic of the article relate to the topic of the dialogue?

Does Birth Order Matter?

Some think there is a link between birth order and personality.

Do you like to compete? You must be a first-born child! Some researchers believe there is a connection between birth order and personality. They argue that being first-born, middle-born, or last-born may determine your personality.

According to some studies, first-born or only children get more attention from parents. They are more responsible and tend to be high achievers who like to compete. Middle children are more affected by rivalry and may be less confident and more rebellious. They may also like to negotiate between siblings. Last-born children have nothing to lose and take more physical risks. They usually get along with others and are artistic.

Is it possible that the instructions children get differ according to birth order? Look at high achieving first-borns like Bill Clinton and billionaire Ted Turner. But what about Venus and Serena Williams? They are the youngest of five sisters and are successful and competitive tennis players. It seems there may be more to personality than birth order.

Talk About It Discuss the questions with a partner or in a group. Think about your place in the birth order. Do you think birth order affects your personality? Why or why not? Circle your opinion. Then, complete the sentence frame.

I think birth order (does/does not) affect my personality

because _____

_____

_____

_____ .

 ELA V 1.4 Monitor expository text for unknown words or words with novel meanings by using word, sentence, and paragraph clues to determine meaning. **(ELD V B2, B4, EI5, I1, EA1) ELA R 2.3** Connect and clarify main ideas by identifying their relationships to other sources and related topics. **(ELD B8, EI9, I9, EA9)**

Language Workshop

FORM & FUNCTION

Important Words

detail: a piece of information
(cognate: detalle)

infer: to assume something based on facts
(cognate: inferir)

Details The article you just read gave many details about how birth order might influence personality. A detail is a piece of information. You can use details to infer about what you read. The following example contains several details.

Example: **Cynthia frowned when she saw her sister win the award.**

Details from the text
Cynthia frowned
She has a sister
Her sister won an award

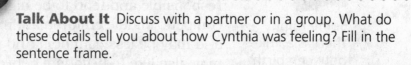

Talk About It Discuss with a partner or in a group. What do these details tell you about how Cynthia was feeling? Fill in the sentence frame.

Cynthia probably frowned because she felt _____

_____

about her sister winning an award.

Extend Language Think about the information and details you just learned from the article, "Does Birth Order Matter?"

What can you infer about Cynthia's relationship with her sister? Fill in the sentence frame.

I think Cynthia is probably _____

than her sister and is frowning because _____

_____

_____

_____

_____

_____

ELA R 2.3 Clarify an understanding of texts by creating outlines, logical notes, summaries, or reports. **(ELD R B9, B11, EI9, I10, EA9)**

Comprehension Workshop

Make Inferences When you combine details with your background knowledge, you can make inferences about the text. An inference is a logical assumption. As you practice making inferences, you can use a diagram to organize information. Here is an example.

Sentence: Using a calm voice, Logan tried once again to make peace between his brother and sister.

• What words in the sentence give clues about Logan?

• What background knowledge do you have about brothers and sisters and trying to help stop an argument?

• What inference can you make about Logan? Combine details with your background knowledge.

Middle children are often good negotiators.

Details	Background Knowledge	Make an Inference
_____	_____	_____
_____	_____	_____
_____	_____	_____

Extend Comprehension Now practice what you have learned. Look for details and use your background knowledge to make inferences. Read the sentences. Then, fill in the diagram.

Maggie put down the phone and let out a loud "Yahoo!" Her sister was coming to visit. Maggie ran to tell her parents the good news.

Details	Background Knowledge	Make an Inference
_____	_____	_____
_____	_____	_____
_____	_____	_____

ELA R 2.4 Clarify an understanding of texts by creating outlines, logical notes, summaries, or reports. (ELD R B9, EI9, EI10, I10, EA9)

Important Words

action verb: a verb that shows the action of a person or thing (cognate: verbo de acción)

linking verb: a verb, like is or feels, that describes a state of being

verb: a word that shows an action or a state of being (cognate: verbo)

Verbs A verb is a word that shows what something is *doing* or how it is *being* in a sentence. An action verb shows what someone is doing. A linking verb connects a noun to a word that describes that noun.

Action Verbs run, jump, think	Linking Verbs is, feels
Example He jumped on his bed.	**Example** Victoria is a musician.

Serena and Venus Williams prove that birth order doesn't determine personality.

Extend Grammar Read each sentence. Underline the verbs in each sentence. Then, write an "A" above the action verbs, or an "L" above the linking verbs.

1. Scientists study people and families.

2. Some scientists believe there is a connection between birth order and personality.

3. Some only children are high achievers.

4. Many oldest children like competition.

5. Some middle children feel less confident.

6. Some middle children negotiate between two sides in an argument.

7. Some last born children become artists.

8. Scientists research how birth order affects personality.

ELA LC 1.0 Students write and speak with a command of standard English conventions appropriate to the grade level. **(ELD LC B8, EI9, I10, EA12)**

Connect to Writing

Sentences with Details Think of all you have learned in this lesson. What new words did you use? How did you learn to use details and background knowledge to make inferences? Talk with a partner about what you learned.

Now practice what you learned. On a separate sheet of paper, write about your personality and how your siblings or other family members shape it. Use details that will help you answer the following questions:

• How would you describe your personality? Why?

• How is your personality shaped by your siblings or other family members? Why?

If you need help, use these sentence frames.

I would describe my personality as _____

_____.

My personality is most shaped by _____

because _____

_____

_____.

Writing Tips
Don't forget to

1. make inferences based on details and background knowledge.

2. use action and linking verbs.

3. use a diagram to organize your information.

Have a Debate Work with some of your classmates. Debate the following question: Does birth order always affect your life? Think of your opinions. Decide what you think. Then, debate your opinions with your classmates.

Tips for Your Debate

• State your opinions in a clear way. State the important parts of your opinions.

• Use facts and examples to support your opinions.

• Organize your opinions and reasons.

• If you don't agree with a classmate's opinions, ask questions.

• If you are listening to a classmate's opinion and don't understand the opinion, provide suggestions.

• After the debate, ask the class which side had better ideas.

 ELA LS 1.4 Select a focus, an organizational structure, and a point of view, matching the purpose, message, occasion, and vocal modulation to the audience. **ELA LS 1.5** Emphasize salient points to assist the listener in following the main ideas and concepts. **ELA LS 2.4** Deliver persuasive presentations. **(ELD B1, B2, B3, EI1, EI2, I1, I3, I4, EA3, EA4, EA5, EA6)**

Vocabulary

Important Words

challenge: something that is difficult and requires extra effort to complete

conclude: to use clues to figure out someting not stated; to form an opinion based on evidence *(cognate: concluir)*

direction: a certain path or way

lose: to fail to succeed; not win

survival: the act or fact of continuing to live or exist

Concept Words

captivity: living in a cage, home, or zoo; not free *(cognate: cautividad)*

hero: someone who saves someone *(cognate: héroe)*

rescue: to save someone or something *(cognate: rescatar)*

Animal Heroes

Dialogue

Two students are talking about animal heroes. Read the dialogue. Then, review the vocabulary words you read.

Student 1: Did you hear about the parrot that rescued the family from a burning house? He must love those people.

Student 2: It was probably an accident. I don't think animals in captivity are that smart.

Student 1: How do you explain the gorilla that saved a three-year-old boy who fell into her zoo cage?

Student 2: You can say what you want. You see an animal hero. I see a gorilla that was headed in that direction and picked up something in its cage.

Student 1: Okay, then explain why a dog would risk his life to save his owner from a falling tree.

Student 2: That's a real challenge, but I don't want to lose this argument. You can conclude he had feelings for him. There's no proof, however, that animals can reason like humans. The only thing animals think about is survival.

Talk About It Discuss the questions with a partner or in a small group. Do you think animals think and feel emotions? How can you tell? Then, complete the sentence frame.

I think animals _____

because _____

_____ .

Read the article. As you read, think about these questions.
- Why do animal heroes save people?
- How does the topic of the article relate to the topic of the dialogue?

ANIMAL HEROES

Could your pet be a hero? Animals have been known to rescue people from danger, even when their own survival is at stake. Cats, birds, and dogs have awakened people in burning homes. Even wild animals in captivity have saved people. At a zoo in Chicago, a gorilla saved a three-year-old boy who fell 18 feet into her exhibit.

So what are animals thinking? These behaviors challenge people's ideas of animals, leading some in the direction of believing that animals have feelings such as love, fear, and stress. How else do you explain a dog that saved his owner, minutes before a huge tree smashed her tent or elephants who have tried to save dying relatives?

Some conclude that these are simple accidents. Certainly not all animals are heroes, and there is no proof that animals can think or reason like humans. But perhaps we have something to learn from animal heroes anyway. Animals who lose their lives for people show us the value of loyalty.

This gorilla saved a three-year-old boy.

Talk About It Discuss the question with a partner or in a small group. Why do you think animal heroes risk their lives for people? Complete the sentence frame.

I think animal heroes risk their lives for people because _____

_____ .

For example _____

_____

_____

ELA V 1.4 Monitor expository text for unknown words or words with novel meanings by using word, sentence, and paragraph clues to determine meaning. **(ELD V B2, EI5, I1, EA1) ELA R 2.3** Connect and clarify main ideas by identifying their relationships to other sources and related topics. **(ELD R B8, EI9, I9, EA9)**

Language Workshop

FORM & FUNCTION

Important Words

background: a person's experience or knowledge; the culture and values with which a person has been raised

infer: to assume something based on facts
(cognate: inferir)

Background Knowledge Background knowledge is knowledge you already have about details in the text, the topic, or the author. Background knowledge can help you infer what is happening in the story.

For example, look at what you can infer from this sentence.

The dog's ears popped up, and she looked at the door and growled.

Detail	**Background Knowledge**	**Make an Inference**
The dog's ears popped up.	Dogs can hear really well.	There's someone at the door.

Talk About It Discuss the question with a partner or in a group. To confirm your inference, you can look for other details in the sentence. What else do you know about dogs? Fill in the rest of the chart.

Detail	**Background Knowledge**	**Make an Inference**
The dog looked at the door and growled.		

Extend Language Now look at the next two sentences.

Suddenly there was a knock at the door and a voice called out the dog's name. The dog jumped up and ran to the door wagging its tail.

Complete the sentence frames. Use details from the sentence and background knowledge about dogs to make an inference.

The dog _____

the voice of the person at the door.

When a dog wags its tail it means _____

_____

The person at the door is _____

ELA R 2.4 Clarify an understanding of texts by creating outlines, logical notes, summaries, or reports.
(ELD R B8, EI9, EI12, I9, EA9)

Comprehension Workshop

Make Inferences An inference is a logical assumption you can make that is not stated in the text. You can make inferences by combining details from the text and your background knowledge. Use a chart to help organize your ideas.

Example: Jasmine hurried past the dog cages to see the rabbits at the show.

Now, complete the rest of the chart. Use your background knowledge to make another inference.

If you need help, think about these questions.

Background knowledge: What is another feeling people have when they hurry?

Inference: How might Jasmine feel about dogs?

Some people believe animals have thoughts and feelings.

Detail	Background Knowledge	Make an Inference
She hurried to see the rabbits.	People are usually excited when they hurry to see something.	Jasmine must like rabbits.
She hurried past the dog cages.		

. . . .

Extend Comprehension Now practice what you have learned. Read the sentences below. Then, fill in the chart. Combine details with your background knowledge to make inferences about how the dogs are feeling.

Two dogs ran up to the fence and barked at us as we walked by. The black dog's tail was wagging. The brown dog was hunched over, baring his teeth.

Detail	Background Knowledge	Make an Inference

ELA R 2.4 Clarify an understanding of texts by creating outlines, logical notes, summaries, or reports. **(ELD R B8, B9, EI9, I9, EA9)**

Grammar

Important Words

principal parts:
the four main forms of
verbs (cognate: partes
principales)

verb: a word that shows
an action or a state of
being (cognate: verbo)

Principal Parts of Verbs Every verb has four main forms,
or principal parts. These forms change in order to show when
something happened. For example, regular verbs form the
past and past participle by adding -ed or -d. Irregular verbs,
such as "be," form their past and past participle in different
ways.

Here are the four forms of the regular verb walk.

Regular verb	
Present	walk
Present participle	(am) walking
Past	walked
Past participle	(have) walked

Extend Grammar Read each sentence. Underline the
verbs. Then, check the correct box.

A: present tense   **B:** present participle
C: past tense   **D:** past participle.

Sentence	A	B	C	D
1. My pet is a hero.				
2. Animals are rescuing people all the time.				
3. Cats, birds, and dogs have awakened people in burning homes.				
4. Wild animals in captivity have saved people.				
5. One gorilla saved a boy at the zoo.				
6. What are animals thinking?				
7. People speculate about animals all the time.				
8. These animals show us the value of loyalty.				

People have a
lot to learn from
animal heroes.

ELA LC 1.0 Students write and speak with a command of standard English conventions approporiate
to the grade level. **(ELD LC B8, EI9, I10, EA12)**

Connect to Writing

Background Knowledge Paragraph How did you learn to use background knowledge to make inferences? Talk with a partner about what you learned.

On a separate sheet of paper, write a paragraph that answers the following questions:

• What background knowledge do you have about animals and their feelings or thoughts? Give examples with details from your own life.

• Based on your experience, how do you explain why animals help people?

Circle your opinion. Then, use the sentence frames.

> I believe animals (do/do not) have feelings or thoughts because
>
> _____.
>
> For example, _____
>
> _____.
>
> Animals probably help people because _____
>
> _____
>
> _____
>
> _____

Present Solutions Work with a partner. Think of some problems some people might have. Then, think of how animal helpers can provide solutions for these problems. What can animal helpers do to help some people's problems?

Tips for Your Presentation

• State your problems and solutions in a clear way. Make sure your listeners follow your main points and ideas.

• Support your problems and solutions with facts and evidence.

• If you can, use pictures of animal helpers to support some of your solutions. Sources like newspapers and reliable Internet sites are good places to find these types of images.

ELA LS 1.5 Emphasize salient points to assist the listener in following the main ideas and concepts. **ELA LS 2.5** Deliver presentations on problems and solutions. **(ELD B1, B2, B3, EI1, EI6, IS, I4, I5, I6, EA3, EA4, EA5, EA8)**

**Lesson 3
Is conflict
always bad?**

Vocabulary

Important Words

battle: a fight or struggle (*cognate: batalla*)

class: a group of students with a teacher (*cognate: clase*)

game: a competition that people do for fun

resolve: to deal with a problem successfully by fixing it (*cognate: resolver*)

win: to succeed; to not lose

Concept Words

achieve: to reach a goal

overcome: to solve a problem or challenge; to be successful

skill: a talent or ability to do something that makes someone special

Challenges

Dialogue

A sports reporter is interviewing Alex Rodriguez about challenges he has overcome. Read the dialogue. Then, review the vocabulary words you read.

Reporter:	Hello, Mr. Rodriguez. Thank you for speaking with us. Today you are very successful at the game of baseball, but as a child you had to overcome many problems. What advice can you give struggling kids?
Rodriguez:	First, you have to build your skills and work hard in class. Never lose sight of your goals and you will achieve them.
Reporter:	Well, you certainly achieved your goals! You make $25 million a year playing baseball. How do you share your success with others?
Rodriguez:	I started a center to help children learn reading, math, and computer skills. I also support my mother and family. You have to remember that everyone faces battles, but the more you resolve to overcome them, the more you will win.

Talk About It Discuss the question with a partner or in a small group. How have the challenges affected Alex Rodriguez? Give examples. Then, complete the sentence frame.

Because of the challenges he faced, Alex Rodriguez _____

_____

_____

For example, _____

_____

_____

_____

Read the article. As you read, think about these questions:
- How does Alex Rodriguez face challenges?
- How does the topic of the article relate to the topic of the dialogue?

A **Winner** On and Off the Field

If you are a baseball fan, you've probably heard of Alex Rodriguez. In his career as a baseball player, Rodriguez has hit more than 500 home runs. His teammates often say, "he makes it look easy." Although baseball may come easy to Rodriguez, he has overcome many challenges to achieve his goals.

As a child, Rodriguez moved a lot, ending up in Miami, Florida with his mother and two siblings. While his mother worked two jobs to support them, Rodriguez worked hard in class and in sports. He resolved to build his natural skills and become a baseball player who wins games for his team. At age 18, he played his first big-league game. Today he makes $25 million playing baseball.

He uses the money to support his mother and help other kids build skills.

But Alex Rodriguez still faces challenges. Many Yankee fans blame him for not bringing the team to the World Series. However, he believes the challenges he battled as a child will help him overcome the challenges he faces today.

Talk About It Discuss the questions with a partner or in a small group. If you could interview Alex Rodriguez, what would you ask? Use the sentence frame. Share your answers.

If I could interview Alex Rodriguez, I would ask _____

_____

_____

_____ .

ELA V 1.1 Read aloud narrative and text fluently and accurately and with appropriate pacing, intonation, and expression. **(ELD V B2, EI5, I1, EA1, EA8) ELA R 2.3** Connect and clarify main ideas by identifying their relationships to other sources and related topics. **(ELD B9, E9, I9, EA9)**

Reading 53

Language Workshop

Important Words

conclude: to use clues to figure out something not stated; to form an opinion *(cognate: concluir)*

question: a sentence that looks for an answer

Questions Asking questions about details in the text can help you conclude or get the full meaning of what the author is trying to say. Questions often start with the words *what*, *who*, *why*, *when*, and *where*.

What happened?
Who was there?
Why did it happen?
When did it happen?
Where did it happen?

Talk About It Read the sentence from the article, "A Winner On and Off the Field." Think about questions that would help you clarify details in the sentence. Fill in the chart.

Sentence: **He believes the challenges he battled as a child will help him overcome the challenges he faces today.**

What battles did he face as a child?

Who _____?

Why _____?

When _____?

Where _____?

Extend Language Work with a partner. How do you think Alex Rodriguez would answer the following question: What battles did you face as a child?

Complete the sentence frame.

I had a hard time as a child because _____

_____

_____

_____

_____.

ELA R 2.7 Make reasonable assertions about a text through accurate, supporting citations.
(ELD R B8, EI9, I9, EA9)

Comprehension Workshop

Draw Conclusions You can draw conclusions by combining the answers to questions with your own background knowledge. Use a diagram to organize your ideas.

Alex Rodriguez still faces challenges. Many Yankees fans blame him for not bringing the team to the World Series.

Ask Questions
Why do they blame Alex?

→

Background Knowledge
He is a great player.

→

Draw a Conclusion
They blame him because they expect a lot from him.

Rodriguez still faces challenges today.

Extend Comprehension Read the sentences from the article, "A Winner On and Off the Field." Ask a question and use your background knowledge to draw a conclusion.

Sentences: Rodriguez worked hard in class and in sports. He resolved to build his natural skills and become a winning baseball player.

Ask Questions

→

Background Knowledge

→

Draw a Conclusion

 ELA R 2.7 Make reasonable assertions about a text through accurate, supporting citations.
(ELD R B8, B9, EI9, I9, EA9)

Grammar

Important Words

simple: easy; not complicated

verb tense: the form of a verb that shows the time of the action or state of being

verb: a word that shows an action or a state of being (*cognate: verbo*)

Simple Verb Tenses A verb is an action word. Verbs are *doing* or *being* words. A verb tense tells *when* an action took place. It is simple to form the past tense of regular verbs. You just add *-ed* or *-d*. You will need to memorize the past tense forms of irregular verbs because they are all different. To form the future tense of both regular and irregular verbs, just add the helping verb *will*.

Tenses	Regular Verb: walk	Irregular Verb: be
present	I walk.	I am.
past	I walked.	I was.
future	I will walk.	I will be.

Extend Grammar Each sentence below is in the present tense. Underline the verbs in each sentence, then rewrite the sentence in both the past and future tenses.

1. Alex Rodriguez makes the right decision.

2. He plays third base for the Yankees.

3. Alex Rodriguez is famous all over the United States.

4. Alex loves baseball.

5. The fans boo Alex.

ELA LC 1.0 Students write and speak with a command of standard English conventions appropriate to the grade level. **(ELD LC B8, EI9, E10, EA12)**

Connect to Writing

Questions How did you use questions and background knowledge to draw conclusions? Talk with a partner about what you learned.

On a separate sheet of paper, write a paragraph that answers the following questions:

- How do questions help you draw conclusions about Alex Rodriguez?
- How does background knowledge help you draw conclusions about Alex Rodriguez?

If you need help, use the sentence frames.

Asking questions helps you draw conclusions by _____

_____.

For example, _____

_____

_____.

Using background knowledge can help you draw conclusions by __

_____.

For example, _____

_____

_____.

Writing Tips
Don't forget to

1. think about how helpful questions can be.

2. use background knowledge.

3. go back and revise your writing.

Rodriguez wants to help struggling kids like him.

· ·

Write an Autobiography or Biography On a separate sheet of paper or on a computer, write an autobiography about a conflict you had to overcome. If you don't want to write about your life, you can write a biography about a character who had to overcome a conflict.

Tips for Your Autobiography or Biography

- For an autobiography, you can write about yourself.
- For a biography, you can write about someone real or someone fictional.
- Include details that explain the conflict. You can organize these details in a chart or you can take notes.
- Use the Writing Process Handbook at the end of this book. This will help you with drafting and revising. If you are writing on a computer, remember to save often and follow the directions for how to use a word-processing program.

ELA W 1.1 Choose the form of writing that best suits the intended purpose. **ELA W 1.5** Compose documents with appropriate formatting by using word-processing skills and principles of design. **(ELD B2, B3, B4, EI2, EI4, I7, EA7)**

Lesson 4
Is conflict always bad?

Vocabulary

Important Words

battle: a fight or struggle (*cognate: batalla*)

challenge: facing something difficult

convince: to make someone feel sure about something (*cognate: convencer*)

perform: to act something out in public using special skills

win: to succeed; to not lose

Concept Words

aggression: an intense energy used against some or something (*cognate: agresión*)

alternative: another option or choice (*cognate: alternativa*)

krumping: an extreme hip-hop dance

Social Groups

Dialogue

Two teenagers are talking about a new dance style. Read the dialogue. Then, review the vocabulary words you read.

Teenager 1: Have you heard of the dance style called krumping?

Teenager 2: Yeah, my brother does it. It's kind of like hip-hop. People put on clown makeup or face paint and do battles. Different groups compete to win.

Teenager 1: That sounds wild. I heard that many people use it as an alternative to fighting.

Teenager 2: My brother does. He is convinced it is a better way to get out his aggression. He lets out his energy and frustration without hurting anybody. My mom and dad are happy because he's off the streets.

Teenager 1: So when is the next krumping battle?

Teenager 2: His crew is being challenged at the battle zone next week. You should come with us.

Teenager 1: Yeah, I would like to see them perform.

Talk About It Discuss the questions with a partner or in a small group. What it is krumping? How is it different from other dances? Use the sentence frame.

Krumping is different from other dances because _____

_____

_____

_____

_____.

Reading

Read the article. As you read, think about these questions:
- How does krumping help people deal with conflict?
- How does the topic of the article relate to the topic of the dialogue?

Krumping Contests: BATTLES WHERE NOBODY GETS HURT

Do you krump? Krumping is a type of dancing that combines hip-hop music, multiple types of movement, competition, and a positive message. Crews of dancers challenge each other in battle zone competitions. The crew that wins walks away with the respect of their peers and their community.

Krumping began in the early 1990s with a man named Tommy Johnson, who performed at birthday parties as "Tommy the Clown." He had a crew of young clowns who added dance moves when they performed. The style gained popularity and soon, krumpers started gathering in small groups to do battles in parking lots, playgrounds, and yards. Today krumping has spread to Europe and Asia, and is seen in music videos and documentaries.

Krumping started with Tommy Johnson in the early 1990s.

Many of the dancers have friends and family members who are involved with gangs and drugs. They are convinced that krumping is a positive alternative to fighting. It helps kids get out their frustrations, anger, and aggressions in a positive way, and keeps them off the streets.

Talk About It Discuss the question with a partner or in a group. If krumping is about battles and aggression, why do teenagers like doing it? Complete the sentence frame.

Teenagers like to krump because _____

_____

_____

_____

_____.

ELA V 1.4 Monitor expository text for unknown words or words with novel meanings by using word, sentence, and paragraph clues to determine meaning. (ELD V B2, EI5, I1, EA1) ELA R 2.3 Connect and clarify main ideas by identifying their relationships to other sources and related topics. (ELD R B8, B9, E9, I9, EA9)

Language Workshop

 FORM & FUNCTION

Important Words

background: a person's experience or knowledge; the culture and values with which a person has been raised

conclude: to use clues to figure out something not stated; to form an opinion based on evidence (*cognate: concluir*)

support: to provide evidence for something

Background Knowledge The article you read concludes that krumping keeps many teenagers out of trouble. If you want to make your own conclusion about krumping, use details from the article and background knowledge to support your conclusion. Background knowledge is information that comes from your own experiences.

Krumping helps kids get out their frustration, anger, and aggressions in a positive way, and keeps them off the streets.

Detail	Background Knowledge	Make an Inference
Krumping keeps kids "off the streets."	Kids hang out on the streets when there is nothing to do. They get into fights and other kinds of trouble.	Krumping can keep kids out of trouble.

Talk About It Work with a partner. Use background knowledge to support the conclusion below. Fill in the background knowledge part of the chart.

Conclusion: **Krumping is a positive alternative to fighting.**

Detail	Background Knowledge	Make an Inference
Crews battle each other in battle zone competitions.		Krumping is a positive alternative to fighting.

Extend Language Read the sentence below. Think about why the krumpers would be respected. Use details from the article and background knowledge to fill in the sentence frames.

Sentence: **The winners of the krump battles are respected by their peers (other teenagers) and community.**

I think other teenagers respect the krumpers because _____

_____. They also respect them

because _____.

I think the community respects the krumpers because _____

_____. They also respect them

because _____.

ELA R 2.4 Clarify an understanding of texts by creating outlines, logical notes, summaries, or reports. (ELD R B8, EI9, I9, EA9)

Comprehension Workshop

FORM & FUNCTION

Draw Conclusions You draw a conclusion when you make up your mind about something. When you read an article, you draw conclusions all the time. Diagrams and charts can help you organize what you are thinking. Read the sentences. Then, fill in the diagram below.

The dancers were very close but not touching. Their movements were strong and aggressive. Their faces looked intense.

• What details give clues about what is happening?

• What background knowledge do you have about the details?

Some say that krumping keeps kids off the streets.

Details from Sentences	Background Knowledge	Draw a Conclusion

Extend Comprehension How would you like to join a krump crew? Use details from the article and your own background experiences to help explain why you would or would not want to join a krump crew. Write your answers in the chart. Then, complete the sentence frame.

Details	Background Knowledge	Conclusion

Conclusion: Joining a krump crew _____ something

I'd like to do because _____

_____.

ELA R 2.4 Clarify an understanding of texts by creating outlines, logical notes, summaries, or reports. **(ELD R B8, EI9, I9, EA9)**

Grammar

Important Words

perfect tense: a form of a verb tense that uses a form of the word *have*

verb: a word that shows an action or a state of being (*cognate: verbo*)

Verbs: Perfect Tenses The perfect tenses are created by combining a form of the helping verb *have* (or *will have*) with the past participle form of a main verb.

- The present perfect tense shows an action that began in the past and continues into the present. (*He has walked a mile.*)

- The past perfect tense shows a past action or condition that ended before another past action began. (*He had walked a mile.*)

- The future perfect tense shows a future action or condition that will have ended before another begins. (*He will have walked a mile.*)

Present Perfect	Past Perfect	Future Perfect
Have, has + past participle	Had + past participle	Will have + past participle
They have finished.	They had finished by the time we arrived.	The dancers will have finished by tomorrow.

Extend Grammar In each sentence below, underline the form of the verb *have* along with the main verb. Then, indicate whether the sentence is A) past perfect, B) present perfect, or C) future perfect by writing A, B, or C above the main verb.

                    A
1. Tommy Johnson <u>had performed</u> as "Tommy the Clown" at kid's parties.

2. He has added dance moves to his clowning.

3. Other crews of young dancers had also appeared.

4. Competitions will have taken place by then.

5. The same dancers have faced each other before.

6. Exciting rivalries have developed.

7. The winners will have received giant belts.

8. Krumping has spread to Europe and Asia.

ELA LC 1.2 Identify and properly use indefinite pronouns and present perfect, past perfect, and future perfect verb tenses; ensure that verbs agree with compound subjects. **(ELD LC B8, EI11, I11, EA12)**

Connect to Writing

Background Knowledge Paragraph How did you use details and background knowledge to draw conclusions? Talk with a partner about what you learned.

On a separate sheet of paper, write a paragraph that answers the following questions:

• What background knowledge did you have about krumping or other details related to this topic? Give examples.

• How did your background knowledge help you draw conclusions about krumping?

If you need help, use these sentence frames.

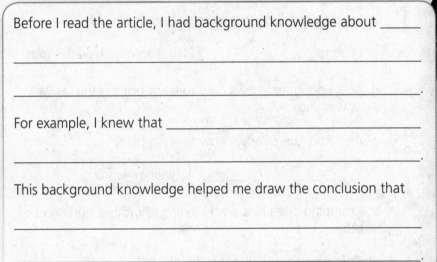

Before I read the article, I had background knowledge about _____

_____

_____.

For example, I knew that _____

_____

_____.

This background knowledge helped me draw the conclusion that

_____

_____

Self-expression is an important part of krumping.

Connect to the Big Question Think about all the articles you read in this unit. What article did you like best? What article did you not like? Then, talk about your favorite article and say what the article was about.

Now, take some time to share your final ideas. Answer this question: Is conflict always bad? Circle your opinion. Then, complete the sentence frame.

I think/do not think conflict is always bad because

_____

_____.

ELA W 2.4 Write responses to literature. **LS 2.3** Deliver oral responses to literature. **(ELD W B2, EI1, I3, I4, EA2, EA3; LS B1, B2, EI1, EI2, I3, I4, EA4, EA5)**

Vocabulary Review

argue

battle

challenge

class

compete

conclude

convince

defend

direction

game

instructions

issue

lose

perform

negotiate

resist

resolve

survival

win

Same Meaning Read the sentences. Fill in the blank with another word that means the same as the vocabulary word.

1. My brother and I had a <u>battle</u> over the TV remote.

   My brother and I had a _____ over the

   TV remote.

2. We discussed <u>issues</u> about birth order.

   We discussed _____ about birth order.

3. I had to <u>conclude</u> that animals have feelings.

   I had to _____ that animals have feelings.

4. Alex Rodriguez knows how to learn from <u>losing</u>, as well
   as winning.

   Alex Rodriguez knows how to learn from

   _____, as well as winning.

5. Krumping gives kids a way to <u>argue</u> without hurting each
   other.

   Krumping gives kids a way to _____

   without hurting each other.

Personal Response Write a response for each sentence.

1. I argue about _____.

2. I try to convince my parents to _____.

3. I feel _____ when my friends challenge me.

4. An issue that is important to me is _____.

5. My favorite game is _____.

ELA V 1.4 Monitor expository text for unknown words or words with novel meanings by using word,
sentence, and paragraph clues to determine meaning. **ELA V 1.5** Understand and explain "shades
of meaning" in related words. **(ELD V B1, B2, EI1, EI2, EI3, I1, I2, EA1, EA2)**

Comprehension Review

Make Inferences An inference is an assumption about a detail or character. Make inferences by combining details with your background knowledge. Read the sentences. Then, complete the sentence frames.

Important Words

background

detail

infer

1. Nita let out a big sigh and slumped in her chair after finishing the test. Based on the details, I infer that Nita

   _____.

2. Marcus dropped the phone and yelled "Yippee!" His brother was coming to town. Marcus feels

   _____ about his brother.

3. Leon used a calm voice to talk his sister out of her room.

   I infer that Leon's sister feels _____.

4. The dog's ears were flat and his teeth showed as he let out a

   low growl. The dog is _____.

5. As Mary pulled into the driveway, the dog ran out wagging

   its tail. The dog feels _____
   to see Mary.

Sports heroes make a difference in people's lives.

Use Inferences Read the sentence. Use your background knowledge and story clues to make an inference. Then, fill in the diagram.

> As Alex Rodriguez passed the bleachers, John jumped up and down, waving his hat and smiling.

Details	Background Knowledge	Inference

ELA R 2.4 Clarify an understanding of texts by creating outlines, logical notes, summaries, or reports. (ELD R B9, EI9, EI10, I10, EA9)

Comprehension Review

Important Words
. . . .
background

conclude

question

support

Draw Conclusions You can draw conclusions by combining the answers to questions with your own background knowledge. Read the passage. Use the diagram to organize your ideas.

Jackson is joining his friends in the Battle Zone Competition. Jackson used to get into a lot of trouble, but now he enjoyes krumping instead. Jackson loves the feeling of dancing with his friends.

Question	Detail (Answer)	Conclusion
1. Who is Jackson's "crew"?		
2. What does Jackson do at the Battle Zone Competition?		
3. Why does Jackson get into less trouble now?		

Best Conclusion Choose the best conclusion based on the details.

1. If Alex Rodriguez faced challenges and is still successful, you can conclude that
   - A. he was saved by someone.
   - B. the challenges weren't very big.
   - C. he has no more problems.
   - D. the challenges made him stronger.

2. If Yankee fans blame Alex Rodriguez for not bringing the team to the World Series, you can conclude that
   - A. the fans don't know him very well.
   - B. he didn't play as well as usual.
   - C. the fans are unfamiliar with baseball.
   - D. he was busy doing other things.

3. If krumping keeps kids out of trouble, you can conclude that
   - A. it is an important form of dance.
   - B. it is only for kids who are in trouble.
   - C. it will replace other forms of dance.
   - D. it will be something adults try.

Krumping keeps kids out of trouble.

ELA R 2.4 Clarify an understanding of texts by creating outlines, logical notes, summaries, or reports. **(ELD R B8, B9, EI9, I9, EA9)**

Choose the Word Complete the sentence. Choose the correct word and write it on the line.

1. Many only children _____ very intelligent.

   (is/are)

2. Scientists _____ how different things

   affect our personalities. (study/studies)

3. Animals have _____ people during

   fires at night. (help/helped)

4. He will _____ the right choice.

   (makes/make)

5. Tommy had _____ at parties.

   (performed/performs)

Replace the Word Replace the underlined word with the word in parentheses. Then, rewrite the sentence. Remember: other words in the new sentence will change as well.

1. Animals have <u>rescued</u> people all over the world. (rescuing)

   _____

   _____

2. He <u>has</u> played for many baseball teams. (will)

   _____

   _____

3. He <u>will</u> be on TV. (has)

   _____

   _____

ELA LC 1.2 Identify and properly use indefinite pronouns and present perfect, past perfect, and future perfect verb tenses; ensure that verbs agree with compound subjects. **(ELD LC B8, EA12)**

Is conflict always bad?

In this unit, I read:

In this unit, I:

- learned new vocabulary words.
- read about different topics.
- identified details.
- used my background knowledge.
- learned about questions.
- learned how to make inferences.
- learned how to draw conclusions.
- learned about verbs.

- learned about the principal parts of verbs.
- learned about simple verb tenses.
- learned about the perfect tenses of verbs.
- wrote sentences with details.
- wrote questions.
- wrote background knowledge paragraphs.

Reflection Think about what you learned in this unit. Complete each sentence frame. Share your answers with your teacher and classmates.

I wonder _____.

I learned _____.

I discovered _____.

I still want to know _____.

I still don't understand _____.

What is important to know?

In this unit, I will read:

In this unit, I will:

- learn new vocabulary words.
- read about different topics.
- use purpose words.
- use questions.
- identify key details.
- learn the difference between important and unimportant details.
- learn about the author's purpose.
- learn about the main idea.

- learn about adjectives and articles.
- learn about comparisons with adjectives.
- learn about adverbs.
- learn about conjunctions and interjections.
- write purpose sentences.
- write questions to determine purpose.
- write a main idea and key details.
- write important details.

What is important to know?

Connect to the Big Question

Answer these questions. Discuss your answers with your teacher and classmates.

> Why is it important to know things?
>
> Does everyone agree on what is important?

. . . .

Extend the Big Question

Read each sentence frame. Write your opinions in each blank.

> I decide what is important by looking at
>
> _____
>
> _____
>
> _____
>
> _____
>
> _____
>
> I know something is not important when
>
> _____
>
> _____
>
> _____
>
> _____
>
> _____

Discuss your opinions with your teacher and classmates.

ELA LS 1.4 Select a focus, an organizational structure, and a point of view, matching the purpose, message, occasion, and vocal modulation to the audience. **ELA LS 1.7** Use effective rate, volume, pitch, and tone and align nonverbal elements to sustain audience interest and attention. **(ELD LS B1, B2, B3, EI1, EI2, EI3, I1, I2, I3, I4, EA1, EA2, EA3, EA4, EA5, EA6)**

Big Question Words

Use your defintions from page 41 of the *Review and Assess* book.

concept
(cognate: concepto)

distinguish
(cognate: distinguir)

examine
(cognate: examinar)

guess

judge
(cognate: juzgar)

knowledge

limit
(cognate: límite)

measure

narrow

observe
(cognate: observar)

purpose

question

refer
(cognate: referir)

source

study
(cognate: estudiar)

Vocabulary Workshop

Same Meaning Write a word that means the same as the Big Question Word.

1. observe _____

2. knowledge _____

3. examine _____

4. limit _____

5. concept _____

Sentence Frames Read each sentence frame. Think about the Big Question Word it contains. Then, complete each sentence.

1. In the dark, I could not **distinguish**

_____

_____

2. He had **narrow** ideas about school uniforms because

_____

_____

3. Paula knew her teacher had reached her **limit** when

_____

_____

4. In school, my favorite subject to **study** is

_____ because

_____

5. To **guess** on a test means to

_____

_____

ELA V 1.4 Monitor expository text for unknown words or words with novel meanings by using word, sentence, and paragraph clues to determine meaning. **ELA V 1.5** Understand and explain "shades of meaning" in related words. **(ELD V B1, B2, EI1, EI2, EI3, I1, I2, EA1, EA2)**

Word Analysis

Suffixes A suffix is a letter or group of letters added to the end of a word. When you add a suffix to the end of a word, you form a new word.

For example, you can add the suffix *-tion* to the word *examine*.

examine + *-tion* = examination

- -

Make New Words Use the suffixes to make new words. Use a dictionary to check your spelling.

Word	Suffix	New Word
limit	-tion	
concept	-tion	
observe	-tion	
judge	-ment	

- -

Words with Multiple Meanings Some words have more than one meaning. For example, the word *flight* can mean many things, including a journey on an airplane, an escape, and a set of stairs.

For each of the words below, write at least two possible meanings. Use a dictionary if you need help.

study
Meanings _____

_____

question
Meanings _____

_____

watch
Meanings _____

_____

bat
Meanings _____

_____

© Pearson Education, Inc. All rights reserved.

ELA V 1.2 Identify and interpret figurative language and words with multiple meanings. **(ELD V B4, EI4, I3, I4, EI5, I8, EA3, EA4, EA5)**

THE BIG ?

Lesson 1
What is important to know?

Vocabulary

Important Words

distinguish: to tell the difference between two things (*cognate: distinguir*)

examine: to look at something very carefully (*cognate: examinar*)

imitate: to act the same way as another person (*cognate: imitar*)

observe: to look closely at someone or something (*cognate: observar*)

purpose: reason; intention; plan

Concept Words

body language: a nonverbal way to communicate, by using parts of your body

nonverbal: not using voice or language (*cognate: no verbal*)

verbal: using your voice or language (*cognate: verbal*)

Communication

Dialogue

The teacher and students are talking about communicating without words. Read the dialogue. Then, review the vocabulary words you read.

Teacher: Today we're talking about body language. As children, we learn to imitate the body language we see in others. Now let's examine it. Body language is nonverbal. Who can give an example of nonverbal body language?

Student 1: Rolling your eyes.

Teacher: Yes, and what does it communicate?

Student 1: Usually making fun of something.

Teacher: Very good. We can also distinguish between body language that is done on purpose and types that are not. Who has observed involuntary body language?

Student 2: Like blushing?

Teacher: Yes! And what does it show?

Student 2: Embarrassment.

Teacher: Yes, but like verbal communication, body language is not universal. The same gestures can mean different things in different countries. Who knows one that is universal?

Student 3: A smile.

Talk About It Work with a partner or in a small group. Think about nonverbal body language. Give an example and explain what it communicates. Then, fill in the sentence frame.

One example of nonverbal body language is _____

_____

It may communicate _____.

Read the article. As you read, think of these questions.
• What is body language? Does it mean the same thing to everyone?
• How does the topic of the article relate to the topic of the dialogue?

THE LANGUAGE OF THE BODY

Imagine you're sitting in class. Are you sitting up straight, or slouching at your desk? What does this tell your teacher? Body language is one of the ways we communicate.

Body language is nonverbal. It does not use words. Verbal language uses words. We can distinguish between body language that is done on purpose, and types that are involuntary like blushing or crying. Body language is something we learn as children. We imitate the gestures of others.

Observe the wide variety of ways people communicate nonverbally: We shake our heads to say "yes" or "no." We open our eyelids wide when we are surprised. We squint when we are unsure.

Most body language is not universal. When you examine it closely, you'll discover that the same gesture can mean something different in other countries, or even in different age groups. For example, most groups in North America expect a young person to look in an older person's face when speaking. In Latin America, this would be considered disrespectful. Fortunately, no matter where you are, a smile is universal.

The eyes are used to express many different emotions.

Talk About It Work with a partner or in a small group. What nonverbal body language do you use when you don't want to do something? Give examples. Then, complete the sentence frame.

When I don't want to do something, I usually _____

_____

_____

ELA V 1.4 Monitor expository text for unknown words or words with novel meanings by using word, sentence, and paragraph clues to determine meaning. **(ELD R B2, B4, EI2, EI5, II1, EA6) ELA R 2.3** Connect and clarify main ideas by identifying their relationships to other sources and related topics. **(ELD B8, B11, EI9, I9, EA9)**

Language Workshop

FORM & FUNCTION

Important Words

entertain: to make happy; to amuse
(cognate: entretener)

inform: to provide someone with facts and details; to communicate information or knowledge to people
(cognate: informar)

persuade: to convince someone of an idea or belief; to change someone's opinion
(cognate: persuadir)

reflect: to think about something; to give something serious thought
(cognate: reflejar)

Purpose Words Purpose words are words that give clues to an author's reason for writing. Authors write to persuade, to entertain, to inform, and to reflect. Understanding the author's purpose will help you better understand what you are reading.

Author's Purpose	Word Clues
To persuade	Strong language like "must," "most," or "best" that favors one side of an issue
To entertain	Silly, humorous, suspenseful, exciting details
To inform or teach	Facts, details, explanations
To reflect on an experience	Description, narration, comments by the writer about his or her past experiences

For example, the author of the sentence below is trying to get teenagers to pay attention to their body language when they talk to grownups. The author believes teenagers should use polite nonverbal language. Underline the clues in the sentence that tell you the author's purpose is to persuade.

• The most important lesson is that children must use polite verbal and nonverbal body language around grownups.

Talk About It Discuss the activity with a partner or in a small group. Choose a purpose for writing. Give examples of the things you could write.

Extend Language Look for purpose words in the sentences below. Decide what the author's purpose may be. Then, circle it.

1. Some studies show that nonverbal communication can be more honest or truer than words.

   Persuade   Entertain   Inform   Reflect

2. As I observed my mother's body language, I realized how much I had inherited from her.

   Persuade   Entertain   Inform   Reflect

3. I think we should buy Project X2, because it is way more exciting than X1.

   Persuade   Entertain   Inform   Reflect

4. The funniest thing happened to me this morning.

   Persuade   Entertain   Inform   Reflect

ELA V 1.4 Monitor expository text for unknown words or words with novel meanings by using word, sentence, and paragraph clues to determine meaning. (ELD R B9, B11, EI9, I12, EA9; V B4, EI4, I7, EA6)

Comprehension Workshop

FORM&FUNCTION

Author's Purpose You can organize information to help clarify what you're reading. Read the passage below. What kind of experience is the author describing? Which author's purpose does it fit best? Find details that support your answer. Then, fill in the chart.

Some body language sends more than one message.

When I first arrived at the party, I saw my friends across the room. They were standing in a circle huddled close together, whispering and looking over their shoulders. As I approached, I heard someone say "sh." Then they all turned and looked at me with forced smiles. I knew they were talking about me.

- What words give clues to the author's purpose?

- What is the author's purpose or reason for writing the paragraph?

Author's Purpose	Details from the Passage

Extend Comprehension Use the article, "The Language of the Body," to fill in the chart below. Remember, an author can have more than one purpose in writing a sentence. For example, a sentence can inform and entertain at the same time. If there are no sample sentences, check the box under No Example.

Author's Purpose	Examples from Article	No Example
To Inform		☐
To Entertain		☐
To Persuade		☐
To Reflect		☐

ELA R 2.4 Clarify an understanding of texts by creating outlines, logical notes, summaries, or reports. **(ELD R B9, EI9, EI10, I10, I12, EA9)**

Grammar

Important Words

adjective: a word that describes a noun or a pronoun *(cognate: adjetivo)*

article: a special adjective; there are three articles: *a*, *an*, and *the* *(cognate: artículo)*

Adjectives and Articles An adjective is a word that describes a noun. Adjectives answer one of the following questions: *What kind? Which one? How many? How much?* An article is a word that is used with a noun to show whether the noun is definite or indefinite. There are three articles: *a*, *an*, and *the*.

Adjectives	Articles
three, broken, pretty	a, an, the
I had three broken pencils.	I had (a) pencil and (an) eraser.
Janet has a pretty smile.	(The) boy smiled.

Extend Grammar Read the sentences. Underline the adjectives and circle the articles.

1. She had a beautiful smile.

2. I asked the friendliest girl to dance.

3. The math teacher held the white chalk in his hand.

4. He has the scariest frown.

5. In response, she turned to me and gave a long sigh.

6. He wears an old baseball cap to work.

7. The angry lion let out a huge roar.

8. She drove away on a red motorcycle.

9. She gave me a beautiful smile.

10. The class has ten desks.

11. The coach threw a red flag.

12. A little rabbit hopped onto the path.

ELA LC 1.0 Students write and speak with a command of standard English conventions appropriate to the grade level. **(ELD LC B8, EI11, I11, EA12)**

Connect to Writing

Writing Tips
Don't forget to
1. be clear about your purpose.
2. use purpose words.
3. go back and revise your writing.

Purpose Sentences What did you learn about understanding an author's purpose? Talk with a partner about what you learned.

Now imagine you are writing your own article about body language. Write a paragraph on a separate sheet of paper. To get started, you might want to use the following sentence frames.

My purpose for writing is to _____ my readers.

I would begin my article by _____

_____.

Then I will write a few sentences about _____

_____.

Crying is an involuntary form of body language.

Research Body Language Work with a partner. Discuss body language. Present information about body language. Explain the different kinds of body language. Then, share your research with the class.

Tips for Your Research

• Think of questions you would want to answer about body language. What are some different types of body language? How does body language help you to communicate?

• Use different sources to find information to answer questions. You can also use these sources to support your opinions. You can use magazines, newspapers, or Internet sources.

• Organize your information. This will help your audience understand what you are saying.

 ELA LS 1.4 Select a focus, an organizational structure, and a point of view, matching the purpose, message, occasion, and vocal modulation to the audience. **ELA LS 1.6** Support opinions with detailed evidence and with visual or media displays that use appropriate technology. **ELA LS 2.2** Deliver informative presentations. (**ELD LS B1, B2, B3, EI1, EI2, EI6, I3, I4, I6, EA4, EA5, EA8**)

Lesson 2
What is important to know?

Vocabulary

Important Words

demand: to ask strongly for something you feel you deserve

integrate: to bring different parts together to make a whole (cognate: *integrar*)

measure: to find out the height, weight, or extent of something

narrow: limited; not broad

purpose: reason; intention; plan

Concept Words

justice: fairness; treating all people equally (cognate: *justicia*)

racial injustice: the limiting of opportunities to people because of their race

tension: strong problems between people (cognate: *tensión*)

Justice

Dialogue

Two students are talking about racial and ethnic justice. Read the dialogue. Then, review the vocabulary words you read.

Student 1: Have you noticed recently, there is a lot of tension and racial injustice at our school?

Student 2: Like what?

Student 1: People from different groups don't get along, and students of color are suspended more often than anyone else.

Student 2: You sound like Martin Luther King, Jr. fighting for justice in the 1960s. Didn't those problems get fixed after they integrated schools?

Student 1: Obviously not, look around! People still have narrow ideas about other groups. People of color are still treated unfairly. I think I'll start a new student group.

Student 2: For what purpose?

Student 1: We will study how students of color are treated unfairly. Then, we'll demand that our school protect the rights of all students. We'll need to measure how much better things get by the end of the year.

Talk About It Work with a partner or in a group. What do you think about racial injustice today? Do you think racial injustice is still a problem? Why or why not? Circle your opinion. Then, complete the sentence frame.

I think racial injustice is/is not _____ still a problem

because _____

_____

_____.

Read the article. As you read, think about these questions:
- What is racial injustice? How are kids working on the problem?
- How does the author try to persuade you?

YOUNG PEOPLE WITH HOPE

Many great steps in the fight against racial injustice were made in the 1960s. Cesar Chavez organized Latino farm workers for better rights and pay. Martin Luther King, Jr. led the struggle to integrate public places and pressured the government to adopt laws like the Civil Rights Act. The American Indian movement was founded to demand rights and justice for Native Americans.

But are things better today? Recent surveys measured Americans' feelings about relationships between different groups. The results showed that some Americans still have narrow views. Many people of color still experience racial and ethnic tension and are treated unfairly. Clearly, the struggle for racial justice continues.

Many groups fought for justice in the 1960s.

One group of teens in Wichita, Kansas is doing their part to bring about change. In 1990, the Hope Street Youth Development group was started with the purpose of helping kids with their homework. Soon they noticed that students of color were suspended from school more often than others. They studied the problem, wrote a report, and made recommendations for fixing the problem. Their report led to changes in the Wichita school system.

Talk About It Discuss the questions with a partner or in a group. If you were going to work on a problem in your school, what would it be? Why is it important to you? Make a list of ideas with your partner. Then, choose one problem to complete the sentence frame.

The author is trying to persuade me because _____.

_____

_____

_____

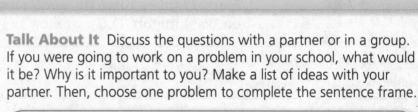

ELA V 1.4 Monitor expository text for unknown words or words with novel meanings by using word, sentence, and paragraph clues to determine meaning. (ELD V B2, B3, EI2, EI5, I1, EA1) ELA R 2.8 Note instances of unsupported inferences, fallacious reasoning, persuasion, and propaganda in text. (ELD R B8, B9, EI9, I9, EA9)

Important Words

determine: to decide something
(*cognate: determinar*)

purpose: reason; intention; plan

question: a sentence that looks for an answer

Questions Asking questions about details in the text can help you understand what you are reading. Questions can also help you draw conclusions or determine the author's purpose. When you want to know the author's purpose, think of the following questions: *what*, *how*, and *why*.

Example: The American Indian movement was founded to demand rights and justice for Native Americans.

What kind of details are presented?	Facts about the American Indian movement
How are the details presented?	Example of a group fighting for justice—very serious
Why does the author present these details in this way?	To inform

Talk About It Work with a partner or in a group. Look at the article, "Young People with Hope." Talk about the group called the Hope Street Youth Development. What else would you like to know about them? Complete the sentence frame.

> If I could ask that group one question it would be _____
> _____.

Extend Language Read the passage below. Use the chart to identify the author's purpose. Decide if it is to entertain, persuade, reflect, or inform. Remember, an author may have more than one purpose.

The 1960s was a powerful time in history when the fight for racial justice was won. Thanks to the efforts of Martin Luther King, Jr. and many others who marched on Washington, D.C., we now have the Civil Rights Act.

What kinds of details are presented?	
How are the details presented?	
Why does the author present these details in this way?	
Author's Purpose:	

ELA R 2.4 Clarify an understanding of texts by creating outlines, logical notes, summaries, or reports.
(ELD B8, B9, EI9, EI12, I10, EA9)

Comprehension Workshop

Cesar Chavez organized
farm workers.

Author's Purpose Look back at the article, "Young People with Hope." What was the author's purpose? Remember that authors can have more than one purpose.

Put a check mark next to the purpose(s) that best reflect what the author had in mind. Then, complete the sentence frame.

___ Inform ___ Persuade ___ Entertain ___ Reflect

Conclusion: The author's purpose(s) was to _____
_____.

I know this because the author _____

_____

_____.

• •

Extend Comprehension Now practice what you have learned. Write about a memorable person or experience you have had. To help you get started complete the sentence frame. Then, use the chart to help you decide what your purpose, or purposes, will be.

I want to write about _____

_____

_____.

What kinds of details will I give?	
How will I present the details?	
Why will I present these details in this way?	

Conclusion: The author's purpose(s) of my writing will be

_____

because _____

_____.

ELA R 2.7 Make reasonable assertions about a text through accurate supporting citations.
(ELD R B8, B9, B11, EI19, EI1, EI11, EI12, EA9) ELA W 1.1 Choose the form of writing that
best suits the intended purpose. **(ELD WS B1, B2, EI1, EI2, I4, EA2, EA3)**

Grammar

Comparison with Adjectives Most adjectives have different forms—the positive, the comparative, and the superlative. Comparative adjectives always compare two nouns. Superlative adjectives compare three or more nouns. A positive adjective describes only one person, place, or thing.

Positive	Comparative	Superlative
I have a *big* problem.	My problem is *bigger* than your problem.	My problem is the *biggest* problem in the neighborhood.
I have a *beautiful* friend.	My friend is *more beautiful* than her friend.	My friend is the *most beautiful* person in the whole school.
The positive describes one person.	The comparative compares two people.	The superlative compares three or more people.

If a positive adjective contains one or two syllables, add the ending -*er* or -*est*. If a positive adjective contains three or more syllables, usually use the words *more* or *most* to form the superlative.

Extend Grammar Complete each sentence. Use the comparative or superlative form of the adjective in parentheses ( ).

1. Some of the _____ steps in the fight against racial injustice were made in the 1960s. (great)

2. Our senator's speech was _____ than our governor's. (short)

3. The survey said African Americans were the _____ group to receive suspensions. (large)

4. The _____ people I know want justice for all. (smart)

5. My friends were the _____ people at the rally. (excite)

6. The March on Washington was one of the _____ civil rights marches of its time. (big)

7. Washington looked _____ that day than ever before. (beautiful)

ELA LC 1.0 Students write and speak with a command of standard English conventions appropriate to the grade level. **(ELD LC B8, I10, EI10, EA12)**

Connect to Writing

Questions to Determine Purpose How did you learn to ask questions to determine the author's purpose? Talk with a partner about what you learned.

On a separate sheet of paper, write two questions you used to determine the author's purpose. How did these questions help you determine the author's purpose?

• What questions did you ask?

• What clues did these questions give you?

If you need help, use these sentence frames. They will help you organize your ideas.

The first question I asked was _____

_____.

The second question I asked was _____

_____.

These questions helped me _____

_____.

Present Solutions Work with a partner. Discuss some of the problems you read in the article on page 81. Then, think of how you can provide solutions to those problems. What can you do to make a difference?

Tips for Your Presentation

• State your problems and solutions in a clear way. Make sure your listeners follow your main points and ideas.

• Support your problems and solutions with facts and evidence.

• If you can, use pictures or other images (like photographs or video clips) to support some of your solutions. Sources like newspapers and reliable Internet sites are good places to find these types of materials.

Writing Tips
Don't forget to

1. think of questions about details.

2. think of questions about purpose words.

3. go back and revise your writing.

Young people can make a difference.

ELA LS 1.5 Emphasize salient points to assist the listener in following the main ideas and concepts. **ELA LS 1.6** Support opinions with detailed evidence and with visual or media displays that use appropriate technology. **ELA LS 2.5** Deliver presentations on problems and solutions. **ELA W 1.3** Use a variety of effective and coherent organizational patterns, including comparison and contrast; organization by categories; and arrangement by spatial order, order of importance, or climactic order. **(ELD LS B1, B2, B3, EI1, EI2, EI6, I3, I4, I5, I6, EA3, EA4, EA5, EA6, EA8; ELD W B2, EI2, I2, EA3)**

Conservation

concept: the idea you have about something based on information *(cognate: concepto)*

devise: to plan, invent, or create

distinguish: to tell the difference between two things *(cognate: distinguir)*

guess: to make an opinion without all the information about something

method: a way of doing something *(cognate: método)*

Concept Words

migrate: to travel a long distance from one place to another *(cognate: emigrar)*

permanent: staying in one place; not moving *(cognate: permanente)*

urban: related to a city *(cognate: urbano)*

Dialogue

A teacher and two students are talking about urban wildlife. Read the dialogue. Then, review the vocabulary words you read.

Teacher:	Today we're talking about urban life and birds. This may be a new concept for you. Who has seen a bird in the city recently?
Student 1:	I see pigeons all the time. They nest on my window.
Teacher:	Yes, pigeons are permanent residents of the city. Others, like songbirds, migrate through the city during the year.
Student 2:	I saw a dead bird yesterday. It hit the library window.
Teacher:	Yes, windows are one of many dangers faced by birds in the city. Some people devised a method for helping birds distinguish between glass and open space. Who can guess what it is?
Student 1:	I've seen stickers on the windows that look like birds.
Teacher:	Exactly! And how do birds help people?
Student 2:	I like to listen to them singing.

Talk About It Work with a partner or in a small group. List ways birds can help people. What other ways do birds help people? Then, complete the sentence frame.

Birds also help people by _____

_____

_____

_____

Read the article. As you read, think about these questions:

- What dangers do birds face in the city?
- How does the topic of the article relate to the topic of the dialogue?

City Life for Birds

When you think of wild birds, you probably think "countryside." In reality, many birds are permanent residents of urban areas, or they migrate through cities during the year. Cities can be a dangerous place for wild birds, but humans have devised new concepts for helping them.

Wild birds in the city face predators, harmful chemicals on plants, and the danger of flying into buildings. Some scientists believe that close to one billion birds are killed every year from crashing into buildings. Some people devised a method to help birds distinguish between glass and open space, which helps reduce deaths.

As you might guess, pigeons are common residents of big cities. But you might not expect to see the peregrine falcon. The falcon is a wild predator that has survived extinction, thanks to a little help from people.

But why the fuss about birds? Birds help humans, too. They spread plant seeds and eat billions of insects a year. And some people still like to hear them sing.

Pigeons are permanent residents of the city.

Talk About It Work with a partner or in a small group. Discuss whether or not people should help birds in the city. Circle your opinion. Then, complete the sentence frame.

I think people (should/should not) help birds in the city because

_____

_____

_____

ELA V 1.1 Read aloud narrative and expository text fluently and accurately and with the appropriate pacing, intonation, and expression. (ELD R B2, B4, EI5, I1, EA1, EA8) ELA R 2.3 Connect and clarify main ideas by identifying their relationships to other sources and related topics. (ELD R B8, EI9, I9, EA9)

Important Words

detail: a piece of information *(cognate: detalle)*

identify: to tell what something is or who owns it; to recognize or point out *(cognate: identificar)*

key: important

Key Details Key details are words or sentences that help you identify the main idea in a passage.

In the paragraph below, key details are in *italics*; the main idea is in **bold**. Look at how the key details all relate directly to the main idea.

Birds are seen migrating over cities every year. *They spread plant seeds*, which help cities stay greener. *They eat billions of insects* every year that carry disease or harm crops. **Birds are an important part of the environment.**

Talk About It Work with a partner or in a small group. Discuss why it is important for cities to stay green. How does that help make cities nice places to live?

Extend Language Look at the sentences in the passage above that are not in *italics* or in **bold**. Think about how these details may support the main idea. Fill in the chart below.

Detail	How It Supports the Main Idea
1. Birds are seen migrating over cities.	
2. Birds help cities stay greener.	
3. Birds eat insects that carry disease or harm crops.	

ELA R 2.4 Clarify an understanding of texts by creating outlines, logical notes, summaries, or reports. **(ELD R B8, B9, B11, EI9, I12, EA9)**

FORM & FUNCTION

Main Idea A web diagram can show how details relate directly to the main idea. Read the passage. Then, fill in the diagram.

In 1970, the peregrine falcon was almost extinct. Some people got together and raised peregrine babies, then released them into urban areas. By 1988, 30 pairs of peregrine falcons were living in several U.S. cities. The cities proved to be great habitats, full of rats and smaller birds to eat. Raising peregrine falcons was sometimes difficult.

Decals, like this one, keep birds from hitting glass windows.

Detail

Main Idea

The city is a great habitat for the peregrine falcon.

Detail

Detail

Detail

- Remember, key details are like building blocks that hold up the main idea.

- The main idea is the most important point in the passage.

Extend Comprehension Use the article, "City Life for Birds," to fill in the chart below.

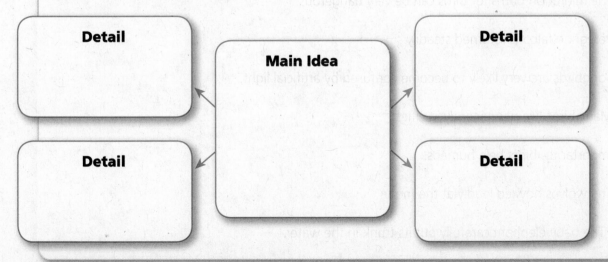

Detail

Main Idea

Detail

Detail

Detail

ELA R 2.4 Clarify an understanding of texts by creating outlines, logical notes, summaries, or reports. **(ELD R B9, B11, EI9, EI10, I10, I12, EA9)**

Grammar

Important Word

adverb: a word that describes a verb, an adjective, or another adverb (cognate: *adverbio*)

Adverbs An adverb is a word that describes or modifies a verb, adjective, or another adverb. Adverbs answer the questions *where*, *when*, *how*, and *to what extent*. Adverbs usually end in *-ly*.

Adverb	Purpose	Question
She walked *slowly*.	modifies *walked*	How did she walk?
She is a *very* strong woman.	modifies *strong*	To what extent is she strong?
She walked *extremely* slowly.	modifies *slowly*	To what extent did she walk slowly?

Many birds migrate through urban cities every year.

Extend Grammar In the sentences below, circle the adverb and underline the word it modifies.

1. She watched the birds fly slowly across the sky.

2. Cities can be extremely deadly for birds.

3. The pigeons eat the seeds very quickly.

4. The migration paths for birds can be very dangerous.

5. Peregrine falcons returned steadily.

6. Songbirds are very likely to become confused by artificial light.

7. Many birds live permanently in cities.

8. Importantly, birds help humans.

9. The wolves howled loudly at the moon.

10. The baby elephant carefully put its trunk in the water.

ELA LC 1.0 Students write and speak with a command of standard English conventions appropriate to the grade level. **(ELD LC B8, EI11, I11, EA12)**

Main Idea and Key Details How did you learn to find key details and the main idea? Talk with a partner about what you learned.

Now, write your own paragraph about an animal that lives in the city. On a separate sheet of paper, write what the main idea of your paragraph will be and three key details. Make sure to answer the following questions:

• Is my main idea clear?

• Do my key details relate directly to my main idea?

If you need help, use the sentence frames. The frames will help you organize your ideas.

The main idea for my paragraph will be _____
_____.

My first detail is _____.

My second detail is _____.

My third detail is _____.

Writing Tips
Don't forget to

1. make sure your main idea is clear.

2. make sure your key details help support the main idea.

3. go back and revise your writing.

Write a Research Report On a separate sheet of paper, write a research report about how people in the city are trying to protect city birds. What examples can you find about this topic? Try to inform your readers with these examples.

Tips for Your Report

• Ask important questions about your topic. Why do people want to help city birds?

• Include specific facts and evidence to support your report. You can use different sources to research facts. Newspapers, magazines, reliable Internet pages, and encyclopedias all contain facts.

• Use the Writing Process Handbook at the end of this book. This will show you how to draft your story. It will also show you how to record information from other sources. Your report should include a bibliography, or a list of your sources.

ELA W 1.2 Create multiple-paragraph expository compositions. **ELA W 1.3** Use a variety of effective and coherent organizational patterns, including comparison and contrast; organization by categories; and arrangement by spatial order, order of importance, or climactic order. **ELA W 2.3** Write research reports. **(ELD W B1, B2, EI3, EI5, I5, I8, I9, EA6, EA8, EA9)**

Lesson 4
What is important to know?

Vocabulary

Important Words

concept: the idea you have about something based on information *(cognate: concepto)*

examine: to look at something very carefully *(cognate: examinar)*

involve: to include or be part of something

narrow: limited; not broad

study: to think, read, and learn about a subject *(cognate: estudio)*

Concept Words

gender: a category that includes male and female *(cognate: género)*

overcome: to solve a problem or challenge; to be successful

stereotype: a belief about a group of people based on knowing only a few *(cognate: estéreotipo)*

Stereotypes and Sports

Dialogue

Two teenagers are talking about the differences between boys and girls playing sports. Read the dialogue. Then, review the vocabulary words you read.

Teenager 1: Did you see Laila Ali on TV last night?

Teenager 2: Yeah, she was great on that dance show.

Teenager 1: No, I'm talking about the boxing match.

Teenager 2: Girls can't be boxers!

Teenager 1: That's a gender stereotype. You can involve girls in the same sports as boys.

Teenager 2: Yeah, but they aren't as strong as boys. People who study gender differences say so. Girls should do sports like gymnastics or cheerleading.

Teenager 1: You have a narrow concept of gender. Examine Laila Ali for a moment. She is a woman who is a good dancer and a great boxer. Think about the stereotypes she has overcome!

Teenager 2: But girls are different from boys. Shouldn't they just compete against each other?

Talk About It Discuss with a partner or in a group. Do you think boys and girls should compete together? Why or why not? Circle your opinion. Then, complete the sentence frame.

> I think boys and girls (should/should not) compete together
>
> because _____
>
> _____
>
> _____

Read the article. As you read, think about these questions:
- What is a gender stereotype?
- Do you agree or disagree with the author's opinion? Why or why not?

Fighting Sports Stereotypes

Laila Ali holds her gloved fists in the air. She just won a boxing championship. Not only is she tough on opponents, she is also overcoming the stereotype that women can't be boxers.

Many people have narrow ideas about gender and sports. People think that football, hockey, and other rough sports are for men, while women should only be involved in cheerleading or gymnastics. These attitudes affect both boys and girls.

Some people believe all sports should be open to everyone, but that girls are physically different and should only compete against girls. Others believe this isn't fair. They think it keeps girls and women out of some sports like football.

Athletes like Laila Ali cause people to examine their concepts about gender and sports. She can be a tough boxer one minute and a graceful dancer on a TV dance show the next minute.

If people study sports stereotypes, maybe the attitudes in the sports world will change just like the faces of the athletes.

Gender stereotypes affect both boys and girls.

Talk About It Discuss with a partner or in a group. Review the article with a partner. Does the author support all the article's opinions? Circle your opinion. Then, complete the sentence frame.

> The author does/does not support all of the opinions in the
>
> article because _____
>
> _____
>
> _____.

ELA V 1.4 Monitor expository text for unknown words or words with novel meanings by using word, sentence, and paragraph clues to determine meaning. **(ELD V B2, B4, EI2, EI5, II1, EA6) ELA R 2.8** Note instances of unsupported inferences, fallacious reasoning, persuasion, and propaganda in text. **(ELD R B8, B11, EI9, I9, EA9)**

Language Workshop

Important Words

important detail: a key piece of information *(cognate: detalle importante)*

main idea: the topic

unimportant detail: a piece of information that is not essential

Important vs. Unimportant To determine the main idea, you must distinguish between important and unimportant details. Important details are words or sentences that tell about the main idea. They are also called supporting details. Unimportant details are pieces of information that may be interesting, but do not directly support the main idea.

Example:

Main Idea	Laila Ali is a great boxer.
Important details	She won a boxing championship. She has trained hard for years. She competes on a regular basis.
Unimportant details	Her father is Muhammad Ali. She danced on TV.

Talk About It Discuss with a partner or in a group. Why do you think Laila Ali decided to become a boxer? Discuss some possible reasons.

Extend Language Read the paragraph below. Decide which sentences are important or unimportant to the main idea. Place each sentence where it belongs in the chart.

Kenyon Smith plays a sport most people think is for girls. He is a synchronized swimmer. He won a high school championship in swimming. He is also a member of the boys' U.S. National team. Kenyon is the only boy on the synchronized swimming team.

Main Idea:	Kenyon Smith challenges stereotypes.
Important Details:	
Unimportant Details:	

ELA R 2.4 Clarify an understanding of texts by creating outlines, logical notes, summaries, or reports. (ELD R B9, EI9, EI12, I9, EA9)

Comprehension Workshop

Main Idea The main idea is the most important point being made in a piece of writing. To determine the main idea, you identify the most important details. Look back at, "Fighting Sports Stereotypes." Use the chart below to identify details that support the article's main idea.

- Ask yourself: Why did the author include this detail?

- Ask yourself: Does this detail help readers understand the main idea of the work?

Laila Ali challenged her own father's stereotypes about women boxers.

Selection: Fighting Sports Stereotypes	
Important Details:	• _____ _____ _____ • _____ _____ _____ • _____ _____ _____
Main Idea:	People are challenging sports stereotypes.

• •

Extend Comprehension Look back at one of the earlier reading selections in this unit. Use the chart to determine the main idea and important details.

Selection:	
Details:	• _____ • _____ • _____
Main Idea:	

ELA R 2.4 Clarify an understanding of texts by creating outlines, logical notes, summaries, or reports. ELA R 2.6 Determine the adequacy and appropriateness of the evidence for an author's conclusions. (ELD R B9, EI9, EI10, I10, I12, EA9)

Grammar

Important Words

conjunction: a word that connects sentence parts *(cognate: conjunción)*

interjection: a word that expresses a feeling, such as pain or excitement *(cognate: interjeción)*

Conjunctions and Interjections Conjunctions connect sentence parts and help group information in a sentence. Interjections express excitement or strong feelings.

Conjunctions	Interjections
and, or, but, nor, for, yet, so	ah, aha, hey, oh, oops, shh, yeah
Example: Laila Ali is good at boxing *and* dancing.	Example: *Aha*! I caught you!

Extend Grammar Write a conjunction or an interjection that fits each sentence.

1. _____! I won the boxing match!

2. Some people think women shouldn't play football

   _____ hockey.

3. Some people think boys shouldn't be synchronized swimmers,

   _____ Kenyon Smith does it anyway.

4. _____, that's not true, that's a stereotype.

5. Stereotypes about gender _____ sports are widespread.

6. _____, I'm sorry, I guess that was a stereotype.

7. Stereotypes keep girls _____ boys outside of some sports.

8. People tease Kenyon, _____ he just says,

   "_____, why don't you give it a try?"

Concepts of gender are changing.

ELA LC 1.0 Students write and speak with a command of standard English conventions appropriate to the grade level. **LC 1.4** Use correct capitalization. **(ELD B8, EI9, I10, EA12)**

Connect to Writing

Writing Tips
Don't forget to

1. determine whether the details support the main idea.

2. use diagrams to help organize your ideas.

3. go back and revise your writing.

Use Important Details How did you learn to distinguish between important and unimportant details to determine the main idea? Talk with a partner about what you learned.

Now write your own paragraph on a separate sheet of paper. Use Kenyon Smith or Laila Ali as your topic. What was your reaction to their stories?

Before you begin writing, complete the sentence frames. Make sure your paragraph has a clear main idea and two important details. Each detail should support the main idea.

The main idea for my paragraph is _____

_____.

One of my details will be _____

_____.

Another detail will be _____

_____.

Connect to the Big Question Think about all the articles you read in this unit. What article did you like best? What article did you not like? Then, talk about your favorite article and say what the article was about.

Now, take some time to share your final ideas. Answer this question: What is important to know? You can complete the sentence frame below. If you like, you can also choose another way to answer the question. Here are some choices: write a letter to a friend or write a brief story about someone who learns a lot of information.

It is important to know _____

_____.

ELA W 1.1 Choose the form of writing that best suits the intended purpose. **LS 2.3** Deliver oral responses to literature. **(ELD W B2, EI1, I3, I4, EA2, EA3; LS B1, B2, EI1, EI2, I3, I4, EA4, EA5)**

Connect to Writing **97**

Big Question Words and Important Words

- concept
- demand
- devise
- distinguish
- examine
- guess
- imitate
- integrate
- involve
- judge
- knowledge
- limit
- measure
- method
- narrow
- observe
- purpose
- question
- refer
- source
- study

Vocabulary Review

Best Answer Read each question. Then, circle the best answer.

1. What is another word for "concept"?
   A. goal   C. limit
   B. idea   D. test

2. Which is an example of "a limit"?
   A. an opinion based on information
   B. an ongoing source of something
   C. a subject that gives you an idea
   D. a point where you must stop

3. Which word refers to the ability to tell the difference between two things?
   A. distinguish   C. survive
   B. guess   D. defend

4. What word has the same meaning as "narrow"?
   A. large   C. unknown
   B. closed   D. special

How do you decide what is important or not important?

Write Sentences Write a sentence for each word.

1. demand _____

_____

2. measure _____

_____

3. guess _____

_____

4. question _____

_____

ELA V 1.4 Monitor expository text for unknown words or words with novel meanings by using word, sentence, and paragraph clues to determine meaning. **ELA V 1.5** Understand and explain "shades of meaning" in related words. **(ELD V B1, B2, EI1, EI2, EI3, I1, I2, EA1, EA2)**

Comprehension Review

Author's Purpose An author can have many purposes for writing a story or article. Read the sentences below. Decide what the author's purpose may be. Then, circle the answer.

1. Some studies show that a smile is universal across the globe.

   Persuade   Entertain   Inform   Reflect

2. The funniest thing happened on the way to school.

   Persuade   Entertain   Inform   Reflect

3. I will show you why this book is better than that book.

   Persuade   Entertain   Inform   Reflect

4. Researchers have determined how birds migrate through cities.

   Persuade   Entertain   Inform   Reflect

5. I used to think that, but now I know it is a stereotype.

   Persuade   Entertain   Inform   Reflect

Important Words

determine

entertain

inform

persuade

purpose

question

reflect

Complete the Chart Read the passage. Then, complete the chart. Try to think of two possible purposes for why the author chose to write the passage.

> Everyone knows that the 1960s was a powerful time for civil rights. Most people think racial injustice ended after President Johnson signed the Civil Rights Act. However, recent surveys show racial tensions are alive and well in the United States. In fact, more than ever, young people should be demanding an end to racial injustice.

Author's Purpose	Details
1.	
2.	

ELA R 2.4 Clarify an understanding of texts by creating outlines, logical notes, summaries, or reports. (ELD R B8, B9, B11, EI9, EI1, EI11, EI12, EA9)

Comprehension Review

Important Words
....
detail

identify

important detail

key

main idea

unimportant detail

Main Idea The main idea is the most important point in a piece of writing. To find the main idea, distinguish between important and unimportant details.

Read the passage. Find the main idea. Then, fill in the chart with the main idea and important details.

> People should protect birds in cities. After all, birds lead difficult lives! Thousands of birds are killed every year, many from flying into buildings. People can help birds distinguish between glass and open space by putting up stickers. Some birds are permanent residents, while others migrate through cities. With a little help from people, more birds can survive.

Detail:

Detail:

Main Idea:

Detail:

Detail:

Important Details Read the passage. Find the main idea. Then, fill in the chart with the main idea and important details.

> Organizations like the Hope Street Youth Development give hope to young people and show them how to make a difference in their communities. At first, some organizations start with a narrow focus. For example, Hope Street started by helping kids with homework. Over time, more young people took on racial justice issues and made a big difference in their communities. Thanks to their work, the school district made changes.

Important Detail:

Main Idea:

ELA R 2.3 Connect and clarify main ideas by identifying their relationships to other sources and related topics. **(ELD R B8, EI9, I9, EA9)**

Grammar Review

Choose the Word Write the correct word on the line to complete the sentence.

Important Words
. . . .
adjective

adverb

article

comparative adjective

compare

conjunction

interjection

positive adjective

superlative adjective

1. He wore _____ old hat to work every day. (a/an)

2. She has _____ beautiful face. (a/an)

3. An _____ lion let out a _____ roar. (big/angry); (massive/incredible)

4. His speech was _____ than hers. (shorter/short)

5. The pigeons ate the popcorn very _____. (quick/quickly)

Pick the Conjunction Choose the right conjunction in the parentheses to combine each pair of sentences into one. Then, write the new sentence with the conjunction.

1. Some people think boys shouldn't dance. My brother dances anyway. (and, or, but)

   _____

   _____

   _____

2. Some people think women shouldn't play football. Others feel boys shouldn't be dancers. (or, and, so)

   _____

   _____

   _____

. . . .

Use Interjections Write one sentence using an interjection. You can use any of the words from the Word Bank.

Word Bank	
ah aha	_____
hey oh	_____
oops shh	_____

ELA LC 1.0 Students write and speak with a command of standard English conventions appropriate to the grade level. **(ELD LC B8, EI11)**

What is important to know?

In this unit, I read:

In this unit, I :

- learned new vocabulary words.
- read about different topics.
- used purpose words.
- used questions.
- identified key details.
- learned the difference between important and unimportant details.
- learned about the author's purpose.
- learned about the main idea.

- learned about adjectives and articles.
- learned about comparisons with adjectives.
- learned about adverbs.
- learned about conjunctions and interjections.
- wrote purpose sentences.
- wrote questions to determine purpose.
- wrote a main idea and key details.
- wrote important details.

Reflection Think about what you learned in this unit. Complete each sentence frame. Share your answers with your teacher and classmates.

I wonder _____.

I learned _____.

I discovered _____.

I still want to know _____.

I still don't understand _____.

Do we need words to communicate well?

In this unit, I will read:

In this unit, I will:

- learn new vocabulary words.
- read about different topics.
- figure out unfamiliar words.
- figure out words with multiple meanings.
- learn to clarify and restate.
- pay attention to punctuation as I read.
- learn about context clues.
- learn to paraphrase.
- learn about simple and compound subjects.

- learn about different sentence types.
- learn about direct and indirect objects.
- learn about predicate nouns and predicate adjectives.
- write about how to figure out unfamiliar words.
- write about how to figure out words with multiple meanings.
- write a simple paraphrase.
- write a complex paraphrase.

Do we need words to communicate well?

Connect to the Big Question
Answer these questions. Discuss your answers with your teacher and classmates.

> What does "communicate" mean to you?
>
> In what ways do people communicate without words?

• • • • • • • • • • • • • • • • • • •

Extend the Big Question
Read each sentence frame. Write your opinions in each blank.

> People communicate without words by _____.
>
> _____
>
> _____
>
> _____
>
> _____
>
> I like to communicate without words by _____.
>
> _____
>
> _____
>
> _____
>
> _____
>
> Discuss your opinions with your teacher and classmates.

 ELA LS 1.4 Select a focus, an organizational structure, and a point of view, matching the purpose, message, occasion, and vocal modulation to the audience. **ELA LS 1.7** Use effective rate, volume, pitch, and tone and align nonverbal elements to sustain audience interest and attention. (**ELD LS B1, B2, B3, EI1, EI2, EI3, I1, I2, I3, I4, EA1, EA2, EA3, EA4, EA5, EA6**)

Do we need words to communicate well?

Big Question Words

Use your definitions from page 61 of the *Review and Assess* book.

communicate
(cognate: comunicar)

connection
(cognate: conexión)

correspond
(cognate: corresponder)

dialogue
(cognate: diálogo)

expression
(cognate: expresión)

gesture
(cognate: gesto)

language:

message
(cognate: mensaje)

nonverbal
(cognate: no verbal)

quote:

reveal
(cognate: revelar)

share:

symbolize
(cognate: simbolizar)

verbal
(cognate: verbal)

visual
(cognate: visual)

Vocabulary Workshop

Use Context Fill in the blanks with Big Question Words.

Sometimes, I have a hard time trying to

_____ my thoughts in my

papers. I sit at the computer for hours, and I wait for

some idea to _____ itself.

I have an easier time in the theater, where

I can use a _____ to show the

audience what I mean. Sometimes in drama,

I have to _____ a character's

words exactly. My favorite part of acting is using

_____ techniques, such

as expressions and movements. I am not a writer.

I am an actor!

- -

Examples and Non-examples Fill in an example and non-example for each of the Big Question Words. Follow the model.

Big Question Word	Example	Non-example
visual	_____	_____
share	_____	_____
language	_____	_____
symbolize	_____	_____
expression	_____	_____
connection	_____	_____

 ELA V 1.4 Monitor expository text for unknown words or words with novel meanings by using word, sentence, and paragraph clues to determine meaning. **ELA V 1.5** Understand and explain "shades of meaning" in related words. **(ELD V B1, B2, EI1, EI2, EI3, I1, I2, EA1, EA2)**

Prefixes Prefixes can give you clues about the meaning of words. A prefix is a group of letters that appear at the beginning of a word. A prefix can help form a new word.

For example, the prefix *non-* means "not". You can add the prefix *non-* to the word *verbal*.

non + verbal = nonverbal

Make New Words Use the prefixes to make new words. Use a dictionary to check your spelling

Word	Prfix	New Word
afraid	un-	
fiction	non-	
sense	non-	
appear	dis-	

This person is making a nonverbal expression.

Idioms An idiom is an expression that combines words to mean something different than what the words mean on their own or separately. Idioms are very common in English. They may seem strange to you when you first hear them. It is important to look for clues to figure out the meaning of idioms. Here are some examples of idioms.

Idiom	Meaning
hold your horses	be patient
a piece of cake	very easy
blow your top	angry; frustrated

Figure Out Meanings Read each idiom. Then, write the meaning of each. Use a dictionary if you need help.

Idiom	Meaning
to wake up on the wrong side of the bed	
raining cats and dogs	
to sleep on it	

Lesson 1
Do we need words to communicate well?

Vocabulary

Important Words

expression: an outward showing of feeling or thought *(cognate: expresión)*

gesture: a physical showing of an idea or feeling *(cognate: gesto)*

nonverbal: not using voice or language *(cognate: no verbal)*

reveal: to let others know about something *(cognate: revelar)*

Concept Words

humor: communication that is meant to be funny *(cognate: humor)*

manipulate: to control or change *(cognate: manipular)*

physical comedy: humor that is based on body movements *(cognate: comedia física)*

Humor

Dialogue

The parent and teenager are talking about making funny faces. Read the dialogue. Then, review the vocabulary words you read.

Parent:	I just saw a TV show about a gurning contest.
Teenager:	What is gurning?
Parent:	It's making funny faces. People at the contest made some of the craziest expressions I've ever seen.
Teenager:	How do they do it?
Parent:	They manipulate their faces into the funniest, scariest, or craziest shapes possible. It reminded me of you, actually.
Teenager:	What do you mean?
Parent:	Well, you have always been good at making funny faces. You're pretty good at physical comedy, too. You show your sense of humor with nonverbal expressions and gestures. Of course, you also reveal other feelings with nonverbal communication.
Teenager:	Like what?
Parent:	Like rolling your eyes and stomping out of the room to show disagreement.
Teenager:	Wow, that's funny. Maybe I should enter a gurning contest.

Talk About It Discuss the question with a partner or in a small group. How do you use nonverbal communication? Give an example. Then, complete the sentence frame.

An example of my nonverbal communication is _____

_____

_____.

Read the article. As you read, think about these questions:
- How do people show humor? Is humor the same for everyone?
- How does the topic of the article relate to the topic of the dialogue?

Life Is a Funny Thing

Do you think this face is funny or scary?

Are you good at gurning? Gurning is a Scottish term for "making a face." In England, contestants compete for who can make the funniest, scariest, or craziest expressions. Like any good comedian, a skilled gurner knows how to use nonverbal facial expressions to show humor.

Most comedians also use other forms of nonverbal communication, such as physical comedy. They make gestures with their bodies by manipulating their arms, legs, shoulders, and hands to reveal certain emotions. A comedian might slump to show sad feelings, or throw his arms up to show excitement. These gestures may not always mean the same things to all people.

Smiles and frowns usually carry the same meaning across the globe. Gestures, however, are different. A gesture that is polite in one country may be rude in another. Comedians must study what is funny to their audiences, then, train their faces and bodies to make those expressions. Can you make funny faces on purpose? It may be harder than it looks.

Talk About It Discuss the questions with a partner or in a small group. Think of your favorite comedians or someone who makes you laugh. How do they make you laugh? Fill in the sentence frame.

They make me laugh by _____

_____

_____.

ELA V 1.4 Monitor expository text for unknown words or words with novel meanings by using word, sentence, and paragraph clues to determine meaning. **(ELD V B2, B4, EI2, EI5, I1, EA6) ELA R 2.3** Connect and clarify main ideas by identifying their relationships to other sources and related topics. **(ELD R B8, B11, EI9, I10, EA9)**

Language Workshop

FORM & FUNCTION

Important Words

clues: things that help you understand something

context: surrounding text or information (cognate: contexto)

define: to state the meaning (cognate: definir)

unfamiliar: unknown; difficult; not easy

Unfamiliar Words The article you just read may have contained difficult or unfamiliar words. To define or unlock the meaning of unfamiliar words you must become a detective. Look for clues in the context—the words and paragraphs that surround the unfamiliar word.

Here is a sentence from the article:

> They make *gestures* with their bodies by manipulating their arms, legs, shoulders, and hands to reveal certain emotions.

The clues to the unfamiliar word *gestures* can be found later in the sentence. Break it down:

Part of Sentence	Clue
They make *gestures* with their bodies.	Gestures are something you make with your body.
by manipulating their arms, legs, shoulders, and hands	Gestures involve moving your arms, legs, shoulders and hands.
to reveal certain emotions	Gestures can show emotions.

Talk About It Discuss the activity with a partner or in a small group. Look at the article and read the sentences surrounding the sentence above. Look for words that give clues, such as other descriptions and examples of gestures. List the clues you found.

_____

_____

Extend Language Now practice what you learned. In the passage below, circle the words that give clues to the meaning of the underlined word. Then, complete the sentence frame.

> In England, contestants compete to see who can make the funniest, scariest, or craziest expressions. A raised eyebrow or a sly grin might say everything.

Based on the passage, the word "expressions" probably means

_____

_____

ELA V 1.4 Monitor expository text for unknown words or words with novel meanings by using word, sentence, and paragraph clues to determine meaning. **(ELD V B4, EI4, EI5, I4, I7, EA3, EA6)**

Comprehension Workshop

Sometimes expressions can reveal emotions better than words.

Context Clues Context clues are hints you find in the words or sentences surrounding an unfamiliar word. They might be descriptions, explanations, or words with the same meaning. Find context clues by asking questions. Then, say the sentence in your own words.

- What kind of word is it?
- What word can I use in place of the unfamiliar word?
- Does the new sentence make sense?

Read this sentence. Then, complete the chart below. Choose one of the questions on this page to help you complete the chart.

She *manipulated* her face into a mask of sadness: mouth turned down, bottom lip out, eyebrows bunched together in the middle.

Unfamiliar Word:	*manipulated*
Question:	
Answer:	
Meaning:	

Extend Comprehension Now practice what you have learned. Read the sentence. Then, fill in the chart below. When you are done, complete the sentence frame.

The comedian revealed her emotions by *slumping* to show sadness, or throwing her arms up to show excitement.

Unfamiliar Word:	*slumping*
Question:	
Answer:	
Meaning:	

I could replace the word *slumping* with the word

_____ and it would make sense.

 ELA R 2.4 Clarify an understanding of texts by creating outlines, logical notes, summaries, or reports. **(ELD R B9, EI9, EI12, I10, I12, EA9)**

Grammar

© Pearson Education, Inc. All rights reserved.

Important Words

compound subject: a subject that contains two or more subjects that share the same verb *(cognate: sujeto compuesto)*

simple subject: the person, place or thing that a sentence is about *(cognate: sujeto simple)*

Sentences: Simple and Compound Subjects

A sentence can contain a simple or compound subject. A simple subject is the person, place, or thing that the sentence is about.

Simple Subject:	babies
Example:	Babies laugh at almost any face you make.

Some sentences have more than one subject. This is called a compound subject. In compound subject sentences, nouns that are subjects are usually connected by conjunctions such as *and*.

Compound Subject:	babies and children
Example:	Babies and children laugh at almost any face you make.

Extend Grammar In the sentences below, underline the subject. Then, label whether the subject is simple "S" or compound "C".

1. England holds the world championship gurning competition._____

2. Contestants have to pull their faces into the funniest, scariest, or craziest expressions possible. _____

3. Thoughts and feelings show on our faces. _____

4. The face isn't the only thing we use to communicate emotions. _____

5. Arms and hands also show others what we feel. _____

6. Standing, sitting, or moving our bodies are also useful ways to communicate. _____

7. Posture and other kinds of nonverbal expression are called body language. _____

8. Comedians use their entire bodies to make an audience laugh. _____

ELA LC 1.1 Use simple, compound, and compound-complex sentences; use effective coordination and subordination of ideas to express thoughts. (ELD LC B8, EI9, EA11, EA12)

Connect to Writing

Writing Tips
Don't forget to

1. think about how you found context clues.

2. ask questions to unlock the meaning of words.

3. go back and revise your writing.

Unfamiliar Words What new words have you learned? What context clues did you use to find their meanings? Talk with a partner about what you learned.

Now it is time to write about what you learned. On a separate sheet of paper, answer the following questions:

• When you first read the article, which words were unfamiliar to you?

• What strategies did you use to find their meanings? (Examples: looking for similar words, definitions, examples, or other clues.)

If you need help, use the sentence frames.

When I first read the article, I did not understand _____

_____.

To find the meaning(s) of the word(s) I _____

_____.

Now I know _____

_____.

Tell a Story Work with a partner. Tell a story about a funny character. Why is this character funny? What does the character do to make people laugh? After you practice telling the story with your partner, share your story with other classmates.

Tips for Your Story

• Give names to your characters.

• Think of the story's events. Also, give your story a setting, or a place where it happens.

• Use your voice correctly as you tell your story. You can use sound words to express funny things in the story. You can also repeat some words and sentences if you think this will make the story funnier. Will repetition of words help you make the story funnier?

ELA LS 1.2 Identify the tone, mood, and emotion conveyed in the oral communication. **ELA LS 1.7** Use effective rate, volume, pitch, and tone and align nonverbal elements to sustain audience interest and attention. **ELA LS 1.8** Analyze the use of rhetorical devices for intent and effect. **ELA LS 2.1** Deliver narrative presentations. (ELD LS B1, B2, EI1, I2, I3, EA1, EA2, EA3, EA5)

Lesson 2
Do we need words to communicate well?

Vocabulary

Important Words

correspond: when two things are alike
(cognate: corresponder)

message: information you give someone in writing or in a signal
(cognate: mensaje)

share: to give away part of what you have

visual: able to be seen
(cognate: visual)

Concept Words

advertiser: someone who makes ads, like TV commercials

consumer: someone who buys things
(cognate: consumidor)

product: something that is made
(cognate: producto)

Imagery and Communication

Dialogue

This teenage girl and boy are talking about advertisements. Read the dialogue. Then, review the vocabulary words you read.

Teen 1: Oh! I like this commercial. That girl is so pretty. I think I'll go buy some of that makeup she's wearing.

Teen 2: Yeah, but look at the visual message advertisers are sending. Do you think you'll look like her if you wear that make up?

Teen 1: No, of course not. It's just a good product. Oh, wait. Here comes another commercial that I like. That guy is so cute. Look at the way he shares his soda with her. That's my favorite soda, too.

Teen 2: You are the perfect consumer. Advertisers must love you. You really get excited about the commercials you see on television.

Teen 1: What do you mean?

Teen 2: They send visual images that correspond to your needs and wants. You want to look good and get the cute guy. So they make these commercials to convince you to buy their products.

Talk About It Discuss the questions with a partner or in a small group. When you like a commercial, does it make you want to buy the product? Why or why not? Circle your opinion. Then, use the sentence frame.

Liking a commercial (does/does not) make me want to

buy the product because _____

_____

_____.

Read the article. As you read, think about these questions:
- How do commercials use visual images to sell a product?
- Do you think advertising is a form of propaganda? Why?

Just Add Ads

Do you watch TV? Ninety percent of Americans share the experience of watching television. If you're one of these people, you've seen commercials. Advertisers spend billions of dollars a year placing visual images in front of you, in the hopes you will buy their products.

Teenagers are a very important consumer group for advertisers. Teens spend billions of dollars a year, and they also influence what their parents buy.

Television is an important tool for advertisers because it can send powerful visual messages. These messages correspond to the needs of teenagers. For example, a cute boy wears the right jeans and all the girls like him. Or a sports star wears a certain shoe that makes him "fly" so it will do

How often do you watch television?

the same for you. Of course these messages aren't true, but they are effective in selling a product.

So how can you resist advertising? Examine the visual messages. Ask yourself: What are they saying? Is the product something you really need or want? Is it worth what you will spend?

Talk About It Discuss the article with a partner or in a small group. What examples of propaganda are in the article? Use the sentence frame to give an example.

One example of propaganda in the article is _____.

It shows _____
_____.

ELA V 1.4 Monitor expository text for unknown words or words with novel meanings by using word, sentence, and paragraph clues to determine meaning. (ELD V B2, B4, EI2, EI3, EI5, I1, I5, EA3) ELA R 2.8 Note instances of unsupported inferences, fallacious reasoning, persuasion, and propaganda in text. (ELD R B8, B9, EI9, EI12, I9, I10, EA9)

Language Workshop

FORM & FUNCTION

Important Words

clues: things that help you understand something

context: surrounding text or information (*cognate: contexto*)

meaning: the definition of a word

multiple: more than one (*cognate: múltiple*)

Words with Multiple Meanings Sometimes words have more than one meaning. We call these words multiple meaning words. To find the right meaning of the word, reread and read ahead to find context clues.

Example: Compare the meaning of *light* in the two sentences.

Context	I like the *light* blue shade, not the dark blue.
Clues	Light is compared to dark.
Meaning	Light refers to color.

Context	The backpack feels as light as a feather.
Clues	Light is compared to a feather.
Meaning	Light refers to weight.

Talk About It Work with a partner or in a small group. On a separate sheet of paper, make a list of all the multiple meaning words you can think of. Try and use each pair of words in a sentence.

Extend Language Practice looking for context clues. Read the sentences below. Then, write the meaning of the underlined word in the sentence frame.

1. We waited for hours to see the show on TV.

   In this context, the word <u>show</u> refers to _____

   _____.

2. I couldn't wait to show my mother the advertisement.

   In this context, the word <u>show</u> refers to _____

   _____.

3. I watch TV every day.

   In this context, the word <u>watch</u> refers to _____

   _____.

4. Did you see the commercial for the new watch?

   In this context, the word <u>watch</u> refers to _____

   _____.

ELA V 1.2 Identify and interpret figurative language and words with multiple meanings. **(ELD V B4, EI4, EI5, EI6, I1, I4, I7, I8, EA3, EA4)**

Comprehension Workshop

FORM & FUNCTION

Context Clues The chart below helps you organize and analyze context clues. You can use it to discover the function and meaning of an unfamiliar word in a sentence. Read the sentence. Find context clues for the word *advertisers*. Then, fill in the chart.

As you fill in the chart think about these questions:

• What is the function of the word *advertisers* in the sentence?

• What context clues hint at a possible meaning?

• Does your possible meaning make sense when you reread the sentence?

Advertisers make ads especially for kids.

| **Context** |
| Advertisers spend billions of dollars a year placing visual images in front of you. |
| **Function in Sentence (noun, verb, adjective)** |
| |
| **Meaning** |
| |

Extend Comprehension Now practice what you learned. Read the passage below. Choose one of the underlined words. Then, fill in the chart.

Television is an important <u>tool</u> for advertisers because it can send powerful visual messages. For example, a sports star wears a certain shoe that makes him "fly" so it will do the same for you. Of course these messages aren't true, but they are <u>effective</u> in selling a product.

| **Context** |
| |
| **Function in Sentence** |
| |
| **Meaning** |
| |

ELA R 2.4 Clarify an understanding of texts by creating outlines, logical notes, summaries, or reports. **(ELD R B9, EI9, EI12, I10, I12, EA9)**

Grammar

Important Words

declarative: a type of sentence that states an idea *(cognate: declarativa)*

exclamatory: a type of sentence that expresses strong emotion *(cognate: exclamativa)*

interrogative: describes a type of sentence that asks a question *(cognate: interrogativa)*

imperative: a type of sentence that gives an order or direction *(cognate: imperativa)*

Sentence Types Sentences can be classified according to what they do. Four types of sentences are declarative, interrogative, imperative, and exclamatory.

Type of Sentence	Sample Sentence	Function	Punctuation
Declarative	Almost 90% of Americans watch TV daily.	States an idea	Period (.)
Interrogative	How much TV do you watch?	Asks a question	Question mark (?)
Imperative	Buy now!	Gives an order or direction	Period (.) or exclamation mark (!)
Exclamatory	The sale was amazing!	Expresses strong emotion	Exclamation mark (!)

Extend Grammar Read the sentences below. Label each sentence "A" (declarative), "B" (interrogative), "C" (imperative), or "D" (exclamatory).

1. Advertisers use billboards and magazine ads. _____

2. Don't open emails from unknown people. _____

3. How much is the youth market worth to advertisers? _____

4. Is something true just because you see it on TV? _____

5. What kind of visual clues sell products? _____

6. You'll look cool in "Rocking" jeans! _____

7. These messages are not actually true. _____

8. If the advertisement shows happy, famous, and cool people, then the product gets a positive image. _____

9. Watch out for misleading advertisements. _____

10. Teenagers are important consumers. _____

Visual images try to convince you to buy a product.

ELA LC 1.0 Students write and speak with a command of standard English conventions appropriate to the grade level. **(ELD LC B8, EI11, I10, EA12)**

Connect to Writing

Writing Tips
Don't forget to

1. think about how some words have multiple meanings.

2. use context clues to define unfamiliar words.

3. go back and revise your writing.

Clues and Words with Multiple Meanings How did you use context clues to understand unfamiliar words or words with multiple meanings? Talk with a partner about what you learned.

On a separate sheet of paper, write the answers to the following questions:

- When you first read the article, which words were unfamiliar to you?

- What strategies did you use for words that have more than one meaning? (Examples: rereading; looking for word function; reading ahead for context clues.)

If you need help, use the following sentence frames.

When I first read the article, I did not understand _____

_____.

To find the meaning(s) of the word(s) I _____

_____

_____.

• •

Research Television Advertising Work with a partner. Discuss the topic of television advertising. Present information about how television advertising persuades and misleads people. What messages do these ads present on TV? Do you think these are good messages? Why or why not? Then, share your research with the class.

Tips for Your Research

- Think of questions you would want to answer about television advertising. Are commercials good or bad for you? Why?

- Use different sources to find information about advertising. You can use magazines, newspapers, or Internet sources. You can even record some actual TV commercials.

- Organize your information. This will help your audience understand what you are saying.

ELA LS 1.9 Identify persuasive and propaganda techniques used in television and identify false and misleading information. **ELA LS 2.2** Deliver informative presentations. **(ELD B1, B2, B3, EI1, EI2, EI4, I1, I3, I4, EA3, EA4, EA5, EA6)**

Vocabulary

Important Words

communicate: to share ideas in a clear way (*cognate: comunicar*)

expression: an outward showing of feeling or thought (*cognate: expresión*)

gesture: a physical movement that shows an idea or feeling (*cognate: gesto*)

message: information you give someone in writing or in a signal (*cognate: mensaje*)

Concept Words

public: the opposite of private; for everyone to use (*cognate: público*)

risky: a bit dangerous; not safe (*cognate: riesgoso*)

skateboarding: a sport that involves riding a short flat board with four wheels

Public Spaces

Dialogue

This teacher is talking with two teens about skateboarding. Read the dialogue. Then, review the vocabulary words you read.

Teacher: Today the city passed a law banning skateboarding in public places. Does anyone have an opinion about this?

Teen 1: Yeah. I usually skate downtown, now I'll have to find somewhere else to skate.

Teen 2: I'm glad. Now skateboarders won't scare me when I'm walking on the sidewalk.

Teacher: The law banning skateboarding definitely communicates a strong message about not damaging public property. What other messages does it send?

Teen 1: That we don't have a right to personal expression.

Teen 2: That skateboarding is considered risky to the public.

Teacher: Yes, those are all possibilities. So what kind of gesture could the city make to teenagers who want to skate, that wouldn't damage public property or make it risky to others?

Teen 1: They could build a skateboard park! Then, we would have a place to go.

Talk About It Discuss the questions with a partner or in a small group. Should skateboarders be allowed to use public spaces? Why or why not? Circle your opinion. Then, complete the sentence frame.

I think skateboarders (should/should not) be allowed to use

public spaces because _____

_____

_____ .

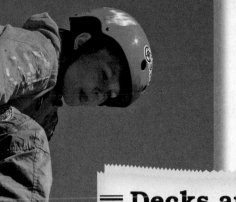

Read the article. As you read, think about these questions:

• Why do skateboarders use public spaces?

• How does the topic of the article relate to the topic of the dialogue?

Decks and Trucks

Are public spaces really for everyone to use? Skateboarders often use public railings, benches, and ramps as places to practice their moves. That is why some city governments view skateboarding as risky and damaging to public property.

As a gesture to skateboarders, some cities are creating skateboard parks with ramps and rails designed specifically for skateboarding. This communicates the message that skateboarding is okay, as long as it doesn't damage public property. Where will skaters go, however, if there isn't a skate park?

To many skateboarders, public spaces are the only option for practicing new moves. Many see skating as not just a sport, but as an expression of personal style. Even when a skateboard park is

Skateboarders practice their moves in public spaces.

available, some may be attracted to public spaces for the thrill of discovering new challenges. Unfortunately for skaters, the fines for getting caught can be expensive.

So if not in public spaces, where should skaters go?

Talk About It Discuss the questions with a partner or in a small group. Why do skateboarders use public spaces? Is it because there are no other options, or is it an expression of personal style? Complete the sentence frame.

I think skateboarders use public spaces because _____

_____

_____

_____.

ELA V 1.4 Monitor expository text for unknown words or words with novel meanings by using word, sentence, and paragraph clues to determine meaning. **(ELD V B2, B4, EI5, I1, EA1) ELA R 2.3** Connect and clarify main ideas by identifying their relationships to other sources and related topics. **(ELD R B8, EI9, I9, EA9)**

Language Workshop FORM & FUNCTION

Important Words

clarify: to make clear
(*cognate: clarificar*)

paraphrase: to restate in your own words
(*cognate: parafrasear*)

passage: a body of text
(*cognate: pasaje*)

restate: to say in another way

Clarify and Restate If you are unsure of the meaning of what you are reading, reread and paraphrase the parts that are difficult. Paraphrasing is a way to clarify, or make clear, what you are reading.

- Reread any difficult lines or passages.
- Look up unfamiliar words and replace them with words you know.
- Restate or paraphrase the sentence or passage using your own words.
- Reread the sentence or passage to make sure that your version makes sense.

Example: **Many see skating as not just a sport, but as an *expression* of *personal style*.**

Unfamiliar word: Meaning:	*expression* outward showing
Unfamiliar phrase: Meaning:	*personal style* one's own way of doing something
Restate sentence:	Many skateboarders like to show their own special way of doing jumps and tricks.

Talk About It Work with a partner or in a small group. How does restating help clarify the meaning of the sentence? Use the sentence frame.

> Restating helps clarify the sentence by _____
>
> _____
>
> _____

Extend Language Read the sentence below and try restating it. Replace the word *gesture* and the phrase *personal style* with your own words.

> As a *gesture* to skateboarders, some cities are creating skate parks with ramps and rails designed specifically for skateboarding. _____
>
> _____
>
> _____

ELA R 2.4 Clarify an understanding of texts by creating outlines, logical notes, summaries, or reports.
(ELD R B8, B9, B11, EI9, EI12, EI14, EA9)

Comprehension Workshop

Paraphrase Paraphrasing is restating something in your own words. Paraphrasing helps clarify what you are reading. Charts can help organize and paraphrase the information you read. Complete the chart. Remember to:

- Reread the sentence to recall and clarify details.
- Look for unfamiliar words and their meanings.
- Restate the sentence in your own words.

Skating can be risky, so many skaters wear protective gear.

Sentence:	Magazines try to communicate the importance of safety to skaters.
Unfamiliar word(s):	communicate
Meaning:	
Paraphrase:	

Extend Comprehension Use the article, "Decks and Trucks," or another article of your choosing. Choose a sentence that has an unfamiliar word(s). Use the chart below to help clarify and paraphrase the sentence.

Sentence:	
Unfamiliar word(s):	
Meaning:	
Paraphrase:	

ELA R 2.4 Clarify an understanding of texts by creating outlines, logical notes, summaries, or reports. **(ELD R B9, B11, EI9, EI10, I10, I12, EA9)**

Grammar

Important Words

direct object: a noun or pronoun that follows an action verb and answers the question *Who?* or *What? (cognate: objeto directo)*

indirect object: a noun or pronoun following an action verb that answers the question *To or for whom?* or *To or for what? (cognate: objeto indirecto)*

Direct and Indirect Objects A direct object is a noun or pronoun that receives the action of a verb. You can identify the direct object by asking "Who?" or "What?"

Example: *Chris rides a skateboard.* (Chris rides *what*?)

An indirect object names the person or thing to whom or for whom an action is done. You can identify the indirect object by asking "for whom" or "to whom?"

Example: *Chris bought a skateboard for Rita.* (Chris bought a skateboard *for whom*?)

Extend Grammar In the sentences below, underline the direct or indirect object. Then, label the direct object "D" or the indirect object "I." The first one is done for you.

1. Skateboarders need ramps. _____

2. Skateboarding parks are used by kids. _____

3. Skateboarders sometimes damage property. _____

4. Skateboarders often receive tickets. _____

5. Most skateboarders wear helmets. _____

6. Skateboarders should watch out for people. _____

7. Tony Hawk promotes skateboarding. _____

8. Skateboarding is fun for boys and girls. _____

9. Yesterday, there was a skateboarding contest. _____

10. The loudest cheer was for the skateboarders. _____

11. The skateboarders formed a club. _____

12. Some skateboarders wear kneepads and gloves. _____

ELA LC 1.0 Students write and speak with a command of standard English conventions appropriate to the grade level. **(ELD B8, EI11, I10, EA12)**

Connect to Writing

Simple Paraphrase How did you learn to paraphrase? Talk with a partner about what you learned. On a separate sheet of paper, choose the first two sentences from one of the paragraphs in the article "Decks and Trucks." Then, paraphrase the sentences.

If you need help use the sentence frames.

Sentences:_____

_____

_____.

These sentences are saying _____

_____.

Writing Tips
Don't forget to

1. reread and read ahead for details.

2. organize your ideas.

3. go back and revise your writing.

This sign bans skateboarding in this public space.

Write an Essay On a separate sheet of paper or on a computer, write an essay about public spaces. Should everyone have a right to public spaces? Do all people respect public spaces? Why or why not? Try to persuade or convince your readers.

Tips for Your Essay

• State your opinions clearly. Use words that will persuade your readers.

• Support your opinions with facts and other evidence. Search the Internet to find facts about your topic.

• Try to include other opinions that are different from your own opinions. The article you read on page 121 can provide some examples.

• Use the Writing Process Handbook at the end of this book. This will help you with drafting and revising. If you are writing on a computer, remember to follow the directions for how to use a word-processing program.

ELA W 1.2 Create multiple-paragraph expository compositions. **ELA W 1.4** Use organizational features of electronic text to locate information. **ELA W 1.5** Compose documents with appropriate formatting by using word-processing skills and principles of design. (ELD W B1, B2, B3, EI2, EI3, EI4, I2, I3, EA2, EA6, EA8, I8)

Lesson 4

Do we need words to communicate well?

Vocabulary

Important Words

communicate: to share ideas in a clear way *(cognate: comunicar)*

dialogue: a conversation between two or more people *(cognate: diálogo)*

nonverbal: not using voice or language *(cognate: no verbal)*

visual: able to be seen *(cognate: visual)*

Concept Words

filmmaker: someone who makes a movie

score: music that goes with a movie or another performance

special effects: sounds and other features that are used in movies *(cognate: efectos especiales)*

Music and Movies

Dialogue

These teens are talking about movie music. Read the dialogue. Then, review the vocabulary words you read.

Teen 1: I'm doing an interview for class about careers. What do you want to be when you grow up?

Teen 2: A filmmaker.

Teen 1: Oh really? And why is that?

Teen 2: I like visual special effects and the way musical scores play with people's emotions.

Teen 1: What kind of movies would you make?

Teen 2: Horror movies, definitely.

Teen 1: Why horror movies?

Teen 2: They don't waste time with a lot of dialogue. They communicate the story through nonverbal effects like creepy sounds and suspenseful music.

Teen 1: That's why I can't stand horror movies. The music always freaks me out.

Teen 2: That's exactly why I like it. Filmmakers know that combining visuals with sound creates a powerful form of communication.

Talk About It Discuss the questions with a partner or in a small group. What do you think about horror movies? How does the music impact your opinion? Complete the sentence frame.

I think the music in horror movies _____

_____

_____

_____

Read the article. As you read, think about these questions:

- How do filmmakers use music? Why does music make a strong impression?
- How does the topic of the article relate to the topic of the dialogue?

MUSICMAGIC

Most people recognize the music from *Jaws*.

Have you seen the movie *Jaws*? If so, you will no doubt recognize the famous "dumDUM dum DUM" musical score that says disaster is about to strike. *Jaws* is a perfect example of how music and visuals add drama to a scene.

Since movies began, filmmakers have used music to communicate emotions in the story. Music is a great nonverbal way to set the mood for a suspenseful moment, an exciting car chase, or a romantic dialogue. Sounds can be used for special effects to make a scene more realistic or creepy. Imagine, without music or sounds, movies might be boring or might not make sense at all.

So why does music make such a strong impression? Some believe music affects the body before our brains can even think about it. Others think that music brings back memories of things in our own lives. Either way, filmmakers have figured out that music and sounds connect to our emotions and are a powerful form of communication.

Talk About It Discuss the questions with a partner or in a small group. What kind of music belongs in a romantic scene? Why? Use the sentence frame to give an example.

_____ music belongs in

a romantic scene because _____

_____

_____.

ELA V 1.4 Monitor expository text for unknown words or words with novel meanings by using word, sentence, and paragraph clues to determine meaning. **(ELD V B2, B3, EI2, EI5, I1, EA1) ELA R 2.3** Connect and clarify main ideas by identifying their relationships to other sources and related topics. **(ELD R B8, B9, EI9, I9, EA9)**

Reading 127

Language Workshop

Important Words

pause: to stop briefly
(cognate: *pausa*)

punctuation: the marks
you see in sentences,
like a *period* or a *comma*
(cognate: *puntuación*)

Punctuation and Fluency Fluency is the ability to read easily and with expression. Punctuation can help you read fluently. End marks, commas, dashes, and semicolons help group words into complete thoughts and can tell you when to pause.

Punctuation	How to Read
no punctuation	Do not pause. Keep reading.
comma (,)	slight pause
colon (:), semi-colon (;), dash (-)	longer pause
period (.), question mark (?), exclamation point (!)	longest pause

Actors have to practice reading their parts aloud.

Talk About It Work with a partner. Take turns reading aloud the sentence below. Use the reading tips in the chart above. Remember to read with expression and pause when needed. Tell your partner how he or she did. Practice reading the sentence until it sounds just the way you want it to.

"I don't like scary movies," said Maria. "The music freaks me out."

Extend Language Read the passage below. Underline the slight pauses and circle the long pauses.

Since movies began, filmmakers have used music to communicate emotions in the story. Music is a great nonverbal way to set the mood for a suspenseful moment, an exciting car chase, or a romantic dialogue.

ELA V 1.1 Read aloud narrative and expository text fluently and accurately and with appropriate pacing, intonation, and expression. (ELD V B1, B2, B3, EI1, EI2, EI6, EI7, I6, EA6)

Comprehension Workshop

Paraphrase Paraphrasing is putting something into your own words. To paraphrase, you must first understand what you are reading. One way to understand is to read aloud according to punctuation.

Read the sentences aloud, pausing with punctuation. Then, write a paraphrase. Complete the chart. Think about the following questions as you read aloud:

• How do pauses help you understand meaning?

• How are ideas grouped?

Sentence	Paraphrase
A musical score is written specifically for a movie, usually as background music.	Musical scores are background music written for movies.
Songs leave an emotional impression, but not for everyone.	
The effect is most powerful when the camera zooms in, the music swells, and the actors say "goodbye."	

Extend Comprehension Now practice what you have learned. Read the passage below, then, paraphrase what you read. Complete the sentence frames.

So why does music make such a strong impression? Some belive music affects the body before our brains can even think about it. Others believe music reminds us of memories of things in our lives.

No one is sure why music affects people. Some say _____

_____

_____

while other think _____

_____

_____

ELA V 1.4 Monitor expository text for unknown words or words with novel meanings by using word, sentence, and paragraph clues to determine meaning. **(ELD V B3, EI4, EI5, I6, EA6, EI8) ELA R 2.3** Connect and clarify main ideas by identifying their relationships to other sources and related topics. **(ELD LR B9, B11, EI9, EI12 I9 EA9)**

Grammar

Important Words

subject complement: a noun, pronoun or adjective that appears with a linking verb

predicate adjective: an adjective that describes the subject of a sentence

predicate noun: a noun that renames or identifies the subject of a sentence

Predicate Nouns and Predicate Adjectives A subject complement is a noun, pronoun, or adjective that says something about the subject of the sentence.

Example: The water *is red*.

There are two types of subject complements: predicate adjectives and predicate nouns. The predicate is the part of the sentence that tells something about the subject. The example above shows a predicate adjective. The adjective (*red*) follows the verb (*is*) and describes the subject (*water*).

The sentence below is an example of a predicate noun. A predicate noun is a noun that renames or identifies the subject. In the example, the noun (*writer*) follows the verb (*was*) and identifies the subject (*William Shakespeare*).

Example: William Shakespeare *was a writer*.

Charlie Chaplin could make audiences laugh and cry.

Extend Grammar A sentence has two main parts, a subject and a predicate. In the sentences below, underline the predicate. Then, label the sentence predicate noun "PN" or predicate adjective "PA."

1. The opening scene from the movie *Jaws* is famous. _____

2. The music from the movie is frightening. _____

3. That music is called a "stinger." _____

4. A "stinger" is a short musical phrase filmmakers use. _____

5. Early films were silent. _____

6. *The Jazz Singer* is considered the first talking picture. _____

7. Al Jolson was talented. _____

8. Early filmmakers were also inventors. _____

9. The first movies were black and white. _____

10. Charlie Chaplin was a famous silent movie star. _____

ELA LC 1.1 Use simple, compound, and compound-complex sentences; use effective coordination and subordination of ideas to express thoughts. **(ELD B8, EI11, I11)**

Connect to Writing

Writing Tips
Don't forget to
1. reread and read ahead for meaning.
2. pay attention to punctuation.
3. go back and revise your writing.

Complex Paraphrase How did you learn to paraphrase? Talk with a partner about what you learned.

On a separate sheet of paper, write at least three sentences that paraphrase the article "Music Magic." Focus on the following questions:

• What is the main idea of the article?

• Why does music make an impression?

If you need help use the sentence frames.

The main idea of the article is _____

_____ .

Some people believe _____

_____ .

Others think _____

_____ .

Before movies had sound, filmmakers played live music in the theaters.

Connect to the Big Question Think about all the articles you read in this unit. What article did you like best? What article did you not like? Then, talk about your favorite article and say what the article was about.

Now, take some time to share your final ideas. Answer this question: Do we need words to communicate well? Circle your opinion. Then, complete the sentence frame.

I think/do not think we need words to communicate well because

_____

_____

_____ .

ELA W 2.4 Write responses to literature. LS 2.3 Deliver oral responses to literature.
(ELD W B2, EI1, I3, I4, EA2, EA3; LS B1, B2, EI1, EI2, I3, I4, EA4, EA5)

THE BIG ?

Big Question Words and Important Words

communicate

connection

correspond

dialogue

expression

gesture

language

message

nonverbal

quote

reveal

share

symbolize

verbal

visual

Vocabulary Review

Choose the Word Circle the word that means the same as the underlined word.

1. My sister will try to <u>communicate</u> with her friend.
   A. expect   C. talk
   B. appear   D. judge

2. He made a wide <u>gesture</u> with his arms.
   A. movement   C. question
   B. purpose   D. guess

3. Her facial expressions <u>correspond</u> with the message she is sending.
   A. communicate   C. distinguish
   B. examine   D. match

4. He is very <u>verbal</u> for his age.
   A visual   C. narrow
   B. talkative   D. realistic

Expressions can say more than words.

Your Own Words Write a definition for these words.

1. connection _____

_____

2. language _____

_____

3. nonverbal _____

_____

4. symbolize _____

_____

ELA V 1.4 Monitor expository text for unknown words or words with novel meanings by using word, sentence, and paragraph clues to determine meaning. **ELA V 1.5** Understand and explain "shades of meaning" in related words. **(ELD V B1, B2, EI1, EI2, EI3, I1, I2, EA1, EA2)**

Comprehension Review

Context Clues Context clues are hints you find in the words or sentences surrounding an unfamiliar word. They might be descriptions, explanations, or words with the same meaning. Find context clues by asking the following questions:

- What kind of word is it?
- What word can I use in place of the unfamiliar word?
- Does the new sentence make sense?

Read the sentence below. Then, complete the chart below. Choose one of the questions on this page to help you complete the chart.

His exact *quote* was, "Getting that space in your brain is what advertisers want."

Unfamiliar Word	*quote*
Question	
Answer	
Meaning	

Important Words

clues

context

define

meaning

multiple

unfamiliar

Multiple Meanings Some words have multiple meanings. Read the sentences below. Then, circle the correct meaning of the underlined word.

1. She and I <u>corresponded</u> by e-mail.
   A. when two things are like   B. a way of communicating

2. They asked me to <u>sign</u> my name.
   A. writing your name   B. a message on the wall

3. Most people <u>watch</u> commercials.
   A. to see something   B. a timepiece

4. The music from the car made a <u>racket</u>.
   A. an instrument for tennis   B. a large amount of noise

5. I'm a big <u>fan</u> of that skateboarder.
   A. an admirer   B. a machine for cooling

ELA V 1.2 Identify and interpret figurative language and words with multiple meanings. **(ELD V B4, EI4, EI5, EI6, I1, I4, I7, I8, EA3, EA4) ELA V 1.4** Monitor expository text for unknown words or words with novel meanings by using word, sentence, and paragraph clues to determine meaning. **(ELD V B4, EI4, EI5, I4, I7, EA3, EA6)**

Comprehension Review

Important Words

clarify

paraphrase

passage

pause

punctuation

restate

Paraphrase Paraphrasing is restating something in your own words. Paraphrasing helps clarify what you are reading. Charts can help organize and paraphrase the information you read. Complete the chart below. Remember to:

- Reread the passage to recall and clarify details.
- Look for unfamiliar words and their meanings.
- Restate the sentence in your own words.

Sentence	Many films use orchestras to communicate feelings like anger, fear, sadness, or happiness.
Unfamiliar Word(s)	communicate
Meaning	
Paraphrase	

Punctuation and Fluency One way to understand what you are reading is to read aloud according to punctuation.

Read the sentences aloud, pausing with punctuation. Then, write a paraphrase. Complete the chart.

Sentence	Paraphrase
Imagine, without music or sounds, movies might not make sense at all.	
"I missed you," she said, then the music swelled and everyone cried.	
Marcus likes car chases in movies, especially when the music is intense.	

ELA R 2.4 Clarify an understanding of texts by creating outlines, logical notes, summaries, or reports. **(ELD R B9, B11, EI9, EI10, I10, I12, EA9) ELA V 1.1** Read aloud narrative and expository text fluently and accurately and with appropriate pacing, intonation, and expression. **(ELD V B1, B2, B3, EI1, EI2, EI6, EI7, I6, EA6)**

Choose the Word Write the correct word on the line to complete the sentence.

1. The movie is _____ ! (film/amazing)

2. _____ something real just because you saw it on TV? (Now, Is)

3. Police often give tickets _____ skateboarders. (at/to)

4. Parents buy helmets _____ their kids. (for/to)

5. _____ kind of things do advertisers use to sell products? (That/What)

Important Words

- compound subject
- declarative
- direct object
- exclamatory
- imperative
- indirect object
- interrogative
- predicate adjective
- predicate noun
- simple subject
- subject complement

Most people know the movie music for a shark attack.

Combine Sentences Combine the two simple subject sentences into one the compound subject sentence.

1. Posture is a kind of body language. Hand gestures are a kind of body language.

   _____

   _____

2. The songs from that movie are famous. The special effects from that movie are famous.

   _____

   _____

3. Al Jolson was talented. Other early performers were talented.

   _____

   _____

ELA LC 1.0 Students write and speak with a command of standard English conventions appropriate to the grade level. **(ELD LC B8, I10, EA12) ELA LC 1.1** Use simple, compound, and compound-complex sentences; use effective coordination and subordination of ideas to express thoughts. **(ELD LC 8, EI9, EA12)**

Do we need words to communicate well?

In this unit, I read:

In this unit, I:

- learned new vocabulary words.
- read about different topics.
- figured out unfamiliar words.
- figured out words with multiple meanings.
- learned to clarify and restate.
- paid attention to punctuation as I read.
- learned about context clues.
- learned to paraphrase.
- learned about simple and compound subjects.

- learned about different sentence types.
- learned about direct and indirect objects.
- learned about predicate nouns and predicate adjectives.
- wrote about how to figure out unfamiliar words.
- wrote about how to figure out words with multiple meanings.
- wrote a simple paraphrase.
- wrote a complex paraphrase.

Reflection Think about what you learned in this unit. Complete each sentence frame. Share your answers with your teacher and classmates.

I wonder _____.

I learned _____.

I discovered _____.

I still want to know _____.

I still don't understand _____.

How do we decide who we are?

In this unit, I will read:

In this unit, I will:

- learn new vocabulary words.
- read about different topics.
- use sequence words.
- infer the sequence of events.
- use compare and contrast words.
- use characteristics.
- learn how to summarize.
- learn how to compare and contrast things.
- learn about prepositions and prepositional phrases.
- learn about the objects of prepositions.
- learn about gerunds.
- learn about gerund phrases.
- write summary sentences.
- write a summary paragraph.
- write compare and contrast sentences.
- write a compare and contrast paragraph.

Connect to the Big Question
Answer these questions. Discuss your answers with your teacher and classmates.

> How do you think about yourself?
> Who are the people in your life that influence who you are?

Extend the Big Question
Read each sentence frame. Write your opinions in each blank.

> I think I am
> _____
> _____
> _____
> _____.
>
> I am most influenced by
> _____
> _____
> _____
> _____
> _____.

Discuss your opinions with your teacher and classmates.

ELA LS 1.4 Select a focus, an organizational structure, and a point of view, matching the purpose, message, occasion, and vocal modulation to the audience. **ELA LS 1.7** Use effective rate, volume, pitch, and tone and align nonverbal elements to sustain audience interest and attention. **(ELD LS B1, B2, B3, EI1, EI2, EI3, I1, I2, I3, I4, EA1, EA2, EA3, EA4, EA5, EA6)**

How do we decide who we are?

Big Question Words

Use your definitions from page 81 of the *Review and Assess* book.

appearance
(cognate: *apariencia*)

conscious
(cognate: *consciente*)

custom
(cognate: *costumbre*)

diverse
(cognate: *diverso*)

expectations
(cognate: *expectativas*)

ideals
(cognate: *ideales*)

individuality
(cognate: *individualidad*)

personality
(cognate: *personalidad*)

perspective
(cognate: *perspectiva*)

reaction
(cognate: *reacción*)

reflect:
(cognate: *reflexionar*)

respond
(cognate: *responder*)

similar
(cognate: *similar*)

trend

unique
(cognate: *único*)

Vocabulary Workshop

Answer the Questions Read each question. Choose a word from the Big Question Words list to answer each question. Write your answer on the line.

1. What word means "point of view"? _____

2. What word means "alike" or "the same"? _____

3. What word is the opposite of "the same"? _____

4. What word describes something that is popular at a certain time? _____

5. What word describes the way someone looks? _____

Complete the Chart Fill in the chart for each Big Question Word. Use the first word as a model.

Important Word	Definition	Examples
individuality	what makes me different from others	my clothes, my favorite music
personality		
unique		
custom		
respond		

ELA V 1.4 Monitor expository text for unknown words or words with novel meanings by using word, sentence, and paragraph clues to determine meaning. ELA V 1.5 Understand and explain "shades of meaning" in related words. (ELD V B1, B2, EI1, EI2, EI3, I1, I2, EA1, EA2)

Word Analysis

Roots Many English (and Spanish) words come from Greek and Latin. Knowing the meaning of common Greek and Latin roots can help you remember word meanings.

For example, the word *perspective* contains the root *-spec-*, which means "look or see". So, *perspective* means "a way of seeing or looking".

What is your perspective?

Write Words Look at the roots in the chart below. Write two words that contain the root. You can use a dictionary to help you.

Root	Meaning	Words
auto	self	
geo	earth	
photo	light	
serve	to serve	
vac	empty	

Words from Other Languages Many English words come from other languages. For example, the word *sumo* is a Japanese word for a specific type of Japanese wrestling.

haiku	opera
ballet	yacht
adobe	

Complete the Sentences Fill in the lines with words from the Word Bank.

1. Bae didn't think he would like _____, because he doesn't speak Italian.

2. Danielle was surprised to see the _____ houses in the Southwest.

3. My mom and I went to see the grace and movement of the

   _____ dancers.

4. This summer, I am going to work as a sailor on a _____.

5. A _____ is a Japanese poem.

ELA V 1.3 Recognize the origins and meanings of frequently used foreign words in English and use these words accurately in speaking and writing. **(ELD V B4, EI4, I3, I4, EI5, EI8, EA3, EA4, EA5)**

Lesson 1
How do we decide who we are?

Vocabulary

Important Words

conscious: deliberate; done on purpose
(cognate: consciente)

expectations: what you think or hope will happen in the future
(cognate: expectativas)

ideals: beliefs or standards of behavior that people use to decide the best way to act
(cognate: ideales)

individuality: a mix of qualities that make you different from other people
(cognate: individualidad)

presume: to expect that something will be a certain way without proof
(cognate: presumir)

Concept Words

excited: happy about something

motivate: to encourage someone to achieve something
(cognate: motivar)

success: happiness; achievement

Self-Motivation

Dialogue

A teacher and students are talking about how people get motivated. Read the dialogue. Then, review the vocabulary words you read.

Teacher: Today we're talking about how people motivate themselves to achieve success. Who can tell me what self-motivation is?

Student 1: It's when you motivate yourself, like when you are excited about something and go do it.

Student 2: I thought it's when you make a conscious decision to do something.

Teacher: You are both correct. How you motivate yourself reflects your individuality. A self-motivated person is aware of their interests and ideals, and they use them to become who they want to be.

Student 1: It's not always that easy. Sometimes things happen outside of your control.

Teacher: That's true. Many people presume that success is the responsibility of each individual. But there are other factors. Can anyone give an example of another factor?

Student 2: Parent expectations make a big difference. Without my mom's support, I couldn't succeed.

Talk About It Discuss the question with a partner or in a small group. Can you think of other factors that lead to success? Use the sentence frame to give an example.

_____

_____

_____ is also a factor that leads to success.

Reading

Read the article. As you read, think about these questions:

- How do you become a success? How do you become self-motivated?
- How does the topic of the article relate to the topic of the dialogue?

THE POWER TO MOVE

Today, Chris Gardner is a successful businessman.

How do you become a success? Do you make a conscious effort, or is it just luck? Some people presume that if you are motivated to succeed, you will. If a person starts life with high ideals, it is possible to succeed despite early struggles with events outside his or her control.

Take Chris Gardner, for example. His mother had high expectations for him. She told him he could be anything. Yet, life as an adult was hard for Chris. First, his son's mother left him, and after that he lost his home. Next, Chris found himself sitting in a public bathroom as a homeless, single father. Although it seemed like a hopeless situation, Chris says it was the moment he started to become a success. He made a conscious decision to move on. Today, he is a successful businessman and the subject of the movie, *The Pursuit of Happyness*.

So what is the secret to his success? Chris recommends finding work that expresses your individuality. Ask yourself, "What do I get excited about?" Set reasonable goals, stay positive, and don't be afraid to ask for help.

Talk About It Discuss the question with a partner or in a small group. What do you think is the secret to success? Use the sentence frame to give two examples.

I think the secret to success is _____

_____

and _____

_____.

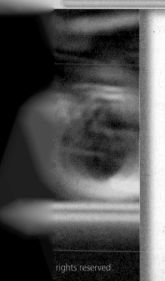

ELA V 1.4 Monitor expository text for unknown words or words with novel meanings by using word, sentence, and paragraph clues to determine meaning. (ELD V B2, B4, EI2, EI3, EI5, II, EA6) ELA R 2.3 Connect and clarify main ideas by identifying their relationships to other sources and related topics. (ELD R B8, B11, EI9, I10, EA9)

Reading 143

Important Words

event: what happens in a story or article

sequence: the order of how events happen (*cognate: secuencia*)

summary: the main ideas in brief form

Sequence Words Most stories have a sequence of events that describes the main idea or most important events in the story. When you learn to identify how events happen in sequence, or in a certain order, it will help you prepare a summary of the text. Here are some sequence words that provide clues to the order of events.

Sequence Words
when
after
next
today
start
then
first

Talk About It Discuss the activity with a partner or in a small group. Look at the chart. Write sequence words that appear in the article, "The Power to Move." Put them in the order in which they appear.

Sequence Words
_____
_____
_____

Extend Language Use the chart and the article to complete the sequence. Decide which sequence words fit best. Then, complete the sentence frames.

Chris Gardner _____ with high expectations, but

other events happened beyond his control.

_____ he lost his partner and his home, he became

a homeless single dad. _____ he decided to change his life.

ELA R 2.7 Make reasonable assertions about a text through accurate supporting citations. **(ELD R B8, EI9, I9, EA9)**

Comprehension Workshop

Summary A summary is a retelling of the main events or main ideas of the text. You can use a chart to help organize a summary of what you are reading. Use the article, "The Power to Move," to fill details into the chart below. Before you begin, read the following suggestions:

- Reread to identify main events in the story.
- List the events in the order they happened.
- Use sequence words in your examples.

Beginning Event			Final Outcome
	→	→	→

· ·

Extend Comprehension Think of your favorite TV show or movie. Use the chart to prepare a summary of one of the shows, or the plot of the movies. Use sequence words when possible.

Beginning Event			Final Outcome
	→	→	→

ELA R 2.4 Clarify an understanding of texts by creating outlines, logical notes, summaries, or reports. **(ELD R B9, B11, EI9, EI12, I10, EA9)**

Important Words

preposition: a word that relates a noun or pronoun to another word in the sentence (*cognate: preposición*)

prepositional phrase: a group of words that begins with a preposition and includes a noun or a pronoun (*cognate: frase preposiocional*)

Prepositions and Prepositional Phrases A preposition is a word that shows the location or relationship between nouns in a sentence. Common prepositions include *in, on, between, by, from, with, at,* and *for.*

Example: **Chris was sitting** *on* **the floor.**
The preposition *on* shows the location of Chris.

A prepositional phrase is the group of words beginning with the preposition, and includes a noun or pronoun.

Example: **Chris was sitting** *on the floor.*
On the floor is the prepositional phrase.

People reach new goals when they are motivated.

Extend Grammar Read the sentences below. Underline the prepositional phrase.

1. In the subway station, Chris made a conscious choice to make a change.

2. Chris never imagined he would end up sitting on that bathroom floor.

3. Love got Chris moving into a new life.

4. After those difficulties, Chris's life began to change.

5. Before his hard times, Chris had a home and a family.

6. Following his partner's departure, he lost his home.

7. Chris hopes that his troubles are safely behind him.

8. Chris knows that what he has learned will help him in the future.

9. Chris says not to be afraid to ask for help.

10. Working with Chris would be fun.

ELA LC 1.0 Students write and speak with a command of standard English conventions appropriate to the grade level. **(ELD LC B8, EI9, EI11, EA12)**

Connect to Writing

Summary Sentences How did you learn to identify sequences and create summaries? Talk with a partner about what you learned.

On a separate sheet of paper, write two sentences that answer the following questions:

- How did you find the sequence of events?
- How did you create a summary?

If you need help getting started, use the sentence frames.

I found the sequence of events by _____

_____

_____

_____

I created a summary by _____

_____

_____

_____

Writing Tips
Don't forget to

1. think about sequence words.

2. think about how you identified the main events.

3. go back and revise your writing.

- -

Research Identity and Attitudes Work with a partner. Discuss what individuality and having a positive attitude mean to you. Look for more information on the effects of a positive attitude. Present your point of view. Explain why a positive attitude can be helpful. Then, share your research with the class.

Tips for Your Research

- Think of questions you would want to answer. How can a positive attitude help someone?

- Use different sources to find information about positive attitudes. You can use magazines, newspapers, or Internet sources. These sources can help you support your opinions and information.

- Organize your information. This will help your audience understand what you are saying.

ELA LS 1.4 Select a focus, an organizational structure, and a point of view, matching the purpose, message, occasion, and vocal modulation to the audience. **ELA LS 1.6** Support opinions with detailed evidence and with visual or media displays that use appropriate technology. **ELA LS 2.2** Deliver informative presentations. (**ELD LS B1, B2, B3, EI1, EI2, EI6, I1, I3, I4, I5, I6, EA3, EA4, EA5, EA8**)

Connect to Writing **147**

Lesson 2
How do we decide who we are?

Vocabulary

Important Words

argument: a reason you give for being in favor of or against something

custom: an action or habit that people take part in on a regular basis (*cognate: costumbre*)

perspective: your point of view, or the way you see and understand something (*cognate: perspectiva*)

reaction: something that happens in answer to something else (*cognate: reacción*)

trend: a pattern of activity or a popular style

Concept Words

enrichment: the act of adding more to your knowledge

overscheduled: when you have way too many things to do at one time

unstructured: not having a plan or a structure (*cognate: desestructurado*)

Time and Activities

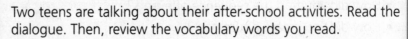

Dialogue

Two teens are talking about their after-school activities. Read the dialogue. Then, review the vocabulary words you read.

Teen 1: Do you want to come over? I got a new video game.

Teen 2: I can't. I have soccer practice and then a piano lesson.

Teen 1: Okay, what about tomorrow?

Teen 2: Nope. I have chess club and karate.

Teen 1: You sound overscheduled. When do you have unstructured time?

Teen 2: Never. My mom thinks I need enrichment activities outside of school. She says it's a custom in our family to stay busy.

Teen 1: My mom's reaction to that would be the opposite. She hates this whole trend of overscheduling. Her argument is that kids need unstructured time to be creative.

Teen 2: What do you do in your free time?

Teen 1: Sometimes I play video games, or listen to music, or maybe nothing at all.

Teen 2: Sounds boring.

Teen 1: Well, that's your perspective. I have a different opinion.

Talk About It Discuss the questions with a partner or in a small group. Which teen from the dialogue are you most similar to? Are you involved in lots of activities, or do you have more free time? Complete the sentence frame.

I am more like _____ because

_____

_____

Read the article. As you read, think about these questions:

- What is the best way to schedule your time?
- How does the topic of the article relate to the topic of the dialogue?

Taking Sides on Time

There may be 24 hours in the day, but how many of those are actual free time? Today, experts have different arguments over how kids should spend their time. A growing trend has left many young people with little free time. Instead, they are participating in more and more scheduled activities. Now people are discussing whether this is a healthy trend.

In reaction to the trend, a doctor named Alvin Rosenfeld wrote a book about kids and their free time. From his perspective, an overscheduled life leads to stress, lack of free play, and pressure to be the best. He believes kids need unstructured free time to be creative.

Others think that organized activities are an important form of enrichment for young people. They believe kids who are not active in

Many people think extra activities are enriching for teenagers.

sports don't get enough exercise. Also, since it is no longer the custom for every family to have one adult at home after school, organized activities keep kids out of trouble. The debate over how much free time kids need is yet to be settled.

Talk About It Discuss the questions with a partner or in a small group. Which type of schedule do you prefer? Why? Complete the sentence frame.

I prefer _____

because _____

_____

_____.

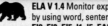

ELA V 1.4 Monitor expository text for unknown words or words with novel meanings by using word, sentence, and paragraph clues to determine meaning. **(ELD V B2, B4, EI2, EI3, EI5, I1, I5, EA3) ELA R 2.3** Connect and clarify main ideas by identifying their relationships to other sources and related topics. **(ELD R B8, B9, EI9, EI12, I9, I10, EA9)** **Reading 149**

Infer Sequence Some sentences begin with sequence words that clearly show the order of events in a story or article. Other events may not include such obvious clues to the order of events. For these events, you must infer sequence by using information found in the text. Listing the sequence of events can help you write the story's summary.

Sequence words
when
after
next
today
start
then

Hilary and Keisha left school together. They both went to soccer practice, then ate pizza with the team. After the pizza, Hilary went home and enjoyed some TV. Keisha went to drama practice and then helped her grandmother shop for groceries.

Talk About It Discuss the activity with a partner or in a small group. Read the above passage. Circle the sequence words. Then, underline the sentences without obvious sequence words. Which of the girls do you think got home the latest? Talk about how you inferred your answer. Then, complete the sentence frame.

I think _____ got home the latest.

I inferred this because _____

_____

_____.

Extend Language Now practice sequencing events. Based on your reading of the passage, number these events in order.

____ They both went to soccer practice.

____ Keisha went to drama practice.

__1__ Hilary and Keisha left school together.

____ Hilary went home and enjoyed some TV.

____ They ate pizza with the team.

____ Keisha helped her grandmother shop for groceries.

ELA R 2.7 Make reasonable assertions about a text through accurate, supporting citations. **(ELD R B8, EI9, I9, EA9)**

Comprehension Workshop

Summary A summary is a short retelling of the main events or main ideas in the text. You can use a chart to help create a summary. Read the passage. Then, fill in the main events in the chart below.

On a typical day, Reggie participates in three different after school activities. Basketball practice is his favorite, which happens right after school. Then, he goes to math club. After that, he often runs home for dinner before going back to school for band practice. If he has energy left, he plays with his little sister. Otherwise, he does his homework and tries to get some sleep to prepare for the next day.

Some kids like being busy, while others find it stressful.

Beginning Event			Final Events

....

Extend Comprehension Use the chart to summarize the article, "Taking Sides on Time." Identify the main ideas in the article.

Beginning Event			Final Outcome

ELA R 2.4 Clarify an understanding of texts by creating outlines, logical notes, summaries, or reports. **(ELD R B8, B9, B11, EI9, EI12, I10, EA9)**

Grammar

Important Words

object of the preposition: the noun or pronoun in a prepositional phrase that is being related to another word in a sentence *(cognate: objeto de la preposición)*

Objects of Prepositions The prepositional phrase is the part of a sentence starting with a preposition that connects to a noun or pronoun.

Example: Sam races to his mom's car.
To his mom's car is the prepositional phrase.

The noun or pronoun in a prepositional phrase is called the object of the preposition. Sometimes, it can show the location of the subject. In the example above, *car* is the object of the preposition, showing the location of the subject, *Sam*.

Some kids feel overwhelmed by so many activities.

Extend Grammar In the sentences below, underline the prepositional phrase. Then, circle the object of the preposition.

1. Sam will have 15 minutes to run from soccer practice.

2. He is hurrying to his violin lesson.

3. Before his next appointment, he will grab a quick snack.

4. He will end the evening in the karate studio.

5. Some people think kids are involved with too many activities.

6. What you do with your time can affect who you are.

7. Dr. Rosenfeld studies kids who at the medical center.

8. Overscheduling can cause problems in children's lives.

9. Kids should ask for help from their parents.

10. In the afterschool program, students learn new skills.

ELA LC 1.0 Students write and speak with a command of standard English conventions appropriate to the grade level. **(ELD LC B8, EI9, EI11, EA12)**

Connect to Writing

Summary Paragraph How did you learn to infer sequences and create summaries? Talk with a partner about what you learned.

On a separate sheet of paper, write a summary of the article, "Taking Sides on Time." As you summarize the article, think of these questions:

• How are the main ideas organized in the article?

• What words can help you write a summary?

If you need help getting started, use the sentence frames.

> "Taking Sides on Time" is about _____
>
> _____ .
>
> The first part of the article _____
>
> _____ .
>
> Later in the article, _____
>
> _____

Writing Tips
Don't forget to

1. think about how you created a summary.

2. use the chart on page 151.

3. go back and revise your writing.

Present Solutions Work with a partner. Provide solutions and instructions for how you can fix someone's overscheduled life. Discuss the advice and think of clear solutions. When you are listening to your partner's presentation, restate the steps he or she suggests for reaching a solution. Then, share your advice with the class.

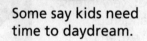

Some say kids need time to daydream.

Tips for Your Presentation

• List your advice in a clear and organized way. Present your advice in steps.

• Try to support your problems and solutions with facts and evidence.

• If you don't understand your partner's advice, ask questions.

 ELA LS 1.3 Restate and execute multiple-step oral instructions and directions. **ELA LS 2.5** Deliver presentations on problems and solutions. **ELA W 2.4** Write responses to literature. **(ELD LS B1, B2, B3, EI1, EI2, EI3, EI6, I3, I4, I6, EA4, EA5, EA8)**

Connect to Writing **153**

Lesson 3
How do we decide
who we are?

Vocabulary

Important Words

appearance: the way someone or something looks or seems to be *(cognate: apariencia)*

calculate: to do math to find an answer or to plan something carefully *(cognate: calcular)*

logical: when something makes sense, follows the rules or is expected *(cognate: lógico)*

personality: the collection of emotions and behaviors that makes someone who they are *(cognate: personalidad)*

respond: to answer a question or do something in return *(cognate: responder)*

Concept Words

extreme: very intense; almost dangerous *(cognate: extremo)*

impossible: very hard to achieve; almost not likely to happen *(cognate: imposible)*

risk: to take a chance

Conquering the "Impossible"

Dialogue

A reporter is interviewing a famous skateboarder. Read the dialogue. Then, review the vocabulary words you read.

Reporter: Today, I'm speaking with pro skater, Andy Mac. Tell us, how did you get involved in extreme sports?

Andy Mac: I was 13 when I first risked a half pipe. After the feel of flying down that 11 foot vertical wall, I was hooked. It became part of my personality.

Reporter: Weren't you scared?

Andy Mac: Oh sure. In fact, I crashed the first time. I looked up at the wall, and it seemed impossible.

Reporter: But you had to respond by trying again?

Andy Mac: Ask anyone about my personality, and they'll tell you I don't give up easily. I came to calculate the dangers and decided to go for it.

Reporter: What did you learn by trying again? There must be a logical reason.

Andy Mac: You'll never know what you can do unless you try. Sometimes appearances can be deceiving. Trying again helps you conquer the "impossible."

Talk About It Discuss the questions with a partner or in a small group. If you crashed on your first try down an 11-foot wall, would you try again? Why or why not? Circle your opinion. Then, complete the sentence frame.

I would/ would not try again because _____

_____

_____

Reading

Read the article. As you read, think about these questions:

- What makes people take extreme risks?
- How does the topic of the article relate to the topic of the dialogue?

Extreme Challenges

At age 15, Alan Gelfand invented the "Ollie."

Would you jump off a building or slide down a mountain? Taking risks is part of life, but some extreme sports athletes take risk to a new level.

Similar to most skateboarders, pro skater Andy Mac was scared the first time he dropped into an 11-foot half pipe. He went airborne, then crashed. The logical thing would be to quit. However, Andy decided to respond by trying again, and he gained confidence.

Skaters, like Alan "Ollie" Gelfand, have come to calculate the risk and conquer the impossible. Gelfand created a famous move called the "Ollie." It is a no-hands way to flip upside-down without the board flying off your feet. The effect gives the appearance of defying gravity.

People used to think climbing the world's tallest mountain was impossible. Now, however, people like Olympic athlete Hannah Teter will snowboard down a mountain as if it was a giant half pipe!

What is it about Hannah or Alan's personality that makes these people try to do the impossible? Is the risk really worth the rewards?

Talk About It Discuss the question with a partner or in a small group. How are people who take risks different from those who don't? Complete the sentence frame.

People who take risks _____

_____

People who don't take risks _____

_____.

ELA V 1.4 Monitor expository text for unknown words or words with novel meanings by using word, sentence, and paragraph clues to determine meaning. **(ELD V B2, B4, EI5, I1, EA1) ELA R 2.3** Connect and clarify main ideas by identifying their relationships to other sources and related topics. **(ELD R B8, EI9, I9, EA9)**

Language Workshop

FORM & FUNCTION

Important Words

alike: the same; similar in appearance

compare: to show how things are alike or similar (*cognate: comparar*)

contrast: to show how things are different (*cognate: contrastar*)

different: not the same (*cognate: diferente*)

similar: alike in some way (*cognate: similar*)

Compare and Contrast Words The article you just read compared and contrasted different extreme sports athletes.

| When you show how two things are similar or alike, you compare them. | When you show how two things are different, you contrast them. |

This chart shows some words you can use to compare and contrast things. Read the chart. Circle the words that appear in the article, "Extreme Challenges."

Comparing Words	Contrasting Words
Both	Different from
Same as	On the other hand
Similar	In contrast to
Just like	As opposed to
Likewise	Unlike
As well as	However

Talk About It Discuss the activity with a partner or in a small group. Use the chart and the article to complete the sentences. Fill in a compare or contrast word. Then, decide if each sentence is comparing or contrasting.

1. _____ to Andy Mac, Alan Gelfand

   take risks. _____

2. Many people never thought snowboarding down mountains

   was possible _____

   Hannah Tete proves them wrong. _____

3. Extreme sports athletes are _____

   people who never try. _____

Extend Language Now create a compare or contrast sentence of your own about the article. How do people who try the impossible compare/contrast with people who never try?

_____

_____

_____

ELA R 2.2 Analyze text that uses the compare-and-contrast organizational pattern. **(ELD R B8, B9, B11, B13, EI9, EI12, EI14, EA9)**

Comprehension Workshop

Compare and Contrast You can organize information to help clarify what you are reading. A Venn diagram can help you compare and contrast information. Use the article, "Extreme Challenges," to compare and contrast Andy Mac and Alan Gelfand. Answer the questions below. Then, fill in the diagram.

• How are the skaters similar?

• How are the skaters different?

Andy Mac
Differences

Similarities

Alan Gelfand
Differences

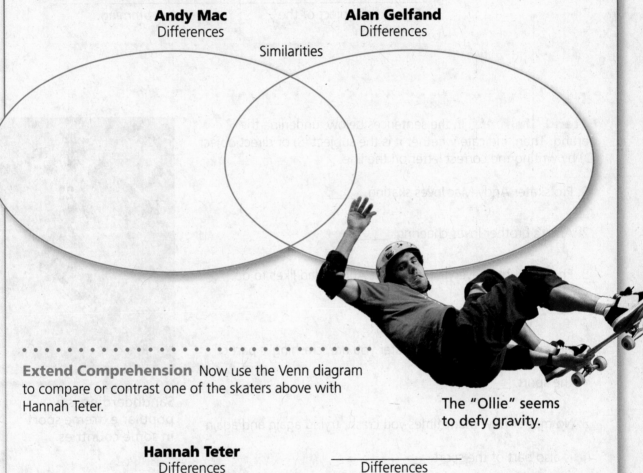

The "Ollie" seems to defy gravity.

Extend Comprehension Now use the Venn diagram to compare or contrast one of the skaters above with Hannah Teter.

Hannah Teter
Differences

Similarities

_____
Differences

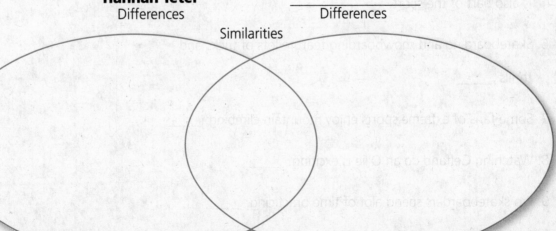

ELA R 2.7 Make reasonable assertions about a text through accurate, supporting citations.
(ELD R B8, B9, B11, B13, EI9, EI12, EI14, EA9)

Grammar

Important Words

gerund: a verb that ends in -ing and is used as a noun (*cognate: gerundio*)

Gerunds A gerund is the form of the verb ending in *-ing*. Even though the gerund is a form of the verb and expresses action, gerunds are special because they act more like nouns in a sentence. Like nouns, they can be subjects, direct objects, and objects of a preposition.

Gerund as subject	*Drumming* is fun.
Gerund as direct object	You love *drumming*.
Gerund as object of the preposition	You live for *drumming*.

Extend Grammar In the sentences below, underline the gerund. Then, indicate whether it is the subject (S) or direct object (D) by writing the correct letter on the line.

1. Pro skater Andy Mac loves skating. _____

2. Andy's brother loves cheering. _____

3. Photographing everything is what Andy's dad likes to do. _____

4. No matter how good of a skater you are, crashing is part of the sport. _____

5. No matter how many times you crash, trying again and again is also part of the sport. _____

6. Skateboarding and snowboarding feature lots of tricks and thrills. _____

7. Some fans of extreme sports enjoy mountain climbing. _____

8. Watching Gelfand do an Ollie is exciting. _____

9. Pro skateboarders spend alot of time practicing. _____

10. Risking injury is part of skateboarding. _____

Sandboarding is a popular extreme sport in some countries.

ELA LC 1.0 Students write and speak with a command of standard English conventions appropriate to the grade level. **(ELD LC B8, EI11, I10, EA12)**

Connect to Writing

Writing Tips
Don't forget to

1. use a Venn diagram to organize your ideas.

2. use words that compare and contrast.

3. go back and revise your writing.

Compare and Contrast Sentences How did you compare and contrast things? Talk with a partner about what you learned.

On a separate sheet of paper, pick two extreme athletes from the article, "Extreme Challenges," and write two compare and contrast sentences that answer the following questions:

• How are the athletes similar?

• How are the athletes different?

If you need help, use the sentence frames. The frames will help you organize your ideas.

_____ is similar to

_____ because

_____

However, they are different because _____

_____

_____ .

Write a Story On a separate sheet of paper, write a story about a character who takes risks. What risk does the character take? What do other characters do in the story? If you need help, you can organize your ideas here.

My Story: _____

Character's Name: _____

Character's Problem: _____

What Other Character's Do: _____

Olympic snowboarder
Hannah Teter
conquers mountains.

Tips for Your Story

Give names to your characters. Also, include a setting for your story, or the place where the story happens.

• Include details and events in your story. Make sure the events are in the right order.

• Use the Writing Process Handbook at the end of this book. This will show you how to draft your story. It will also show you how to revise your story.

ELA W 1.3 Use a variety of effective and coherent organizational patterns, including comparison and contrast; organization by categories; and arrangement by spatial order, order of importance, or climatic order. **ELA W 1.6** Revise writing to improve the organization and consistency of ideas within and between paragraphs. **ELA W 2.1** Write narratives. (ELD B1, B2, B3, B4, EI2, EI4, I1, I2, EA1, EA)

THE BIG ?

Lesson 4
How do we decide
who we are?

Vocabulary

Important Words

discover: to find out about something for the first time (*cognate: descubrir*)

diverse: different from one another, various (*cognate: diverso*)

reflect: to give something serious thought (*cognate: reflexionar*)

similar: alike in some way (*cognate: similar*)

unique: one of a kind, special (*cognate: único*)

Concept Words

connection: a link between two things, people or ideas (*cognate: conexión*)

creative: able to make new ideas easily from the imagination (*cognate: creativo*)

invention: a creation that comes from studying and experimenting (*cognate: invención*)

Creativity

Dialogue

These teens are talking about creative people. Read the dialogue. Then, review the vocabulary words you read.

Teen 1: What inventor are you going to include in your report?

Teen 2: I'm talking about Philo Farnsworth. He was only 14 when he came to discover an idea that led to the invention of television.

Teen 1: How did he do that?

Teen 2: He made a connection between plowing a field back and forth and a way to scan pictures for TV.

Teen 1: Wow, I wish I could be that creative.

Teen 2: Well, I think you can if you open your mind. All this guy did was reflect on how two things were similar.

Teen 1: Yeah, but making connections between plowing a field and a TV is pretty unique.

Teen 2: Anyone can brainstorm diverse possibilities.

Teen 1: Oh really? Then, what's your next creative invention?

Talk About It Discuss the following question with a partner or in a small group: Are inventors all geniuses, or can anyone be an inventor? Circle your opinion. Then, complete the sentence frame.

I do/ do not think that anyone can be an inventor _____

_____

_____

_____

Read the article. As you read, think about these questions:

- What do these inventors have in common?
- How does the topic of the article relate to the topic of the dialogue?

ᴐ The Creative Connection ᴐ

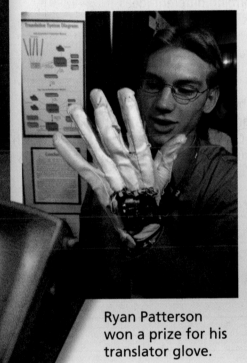

Ryan Patterson won a prize for his translator glove.

What's the connection between a potato field and a television? Ask Philo Farnsworth. At the age of 14, he came to discover the idea for the TV picture tube while plowing a field.

It was 1921. Philo loved science and knew people were working on making a television. While plowing the field back and forth, Philo found time to reflect on a new idea for scanning pictures. His creative idea led to the development of the TV.

Another teen with a unique invention was Ryan Patterson. While standing in line for a hamburger, Ryan watched a deaf customer trying to order his meal by spelling words with his fingers. Then, Ryan noticed the clerk's computer ordering screen. Ryan connected the two and invented a glove that can translate American Sign Language into words on a computer screen.

These teens seem like geniuses, but everyone is capable of creative thinking. Inventors tell us to: Keep an open mind; brainstorm diverse possibilities; be curious; make connections, and recognize how different things are similar. Get ready to be the next great inventor!

Talk About It Discuss the question with a partner or in a small group. How do inventors make creative connections? Complete the sentence frame.

Inventors make creative connections by _____

_____

_____.

 ELA V 1.4 Monitor expository text for unknown words or words with novel meanings by using word, sentence, and paragraph clues to determine meaning. **(ELD V B2, B3, EI2, EI5, I1, EA1) ELA R 2.3** Connect and clarify main ideas by identifying their relationships to other sources and related topics. **(ELD R B8, B9, EI9, I9, EA9)**

Language Workshop

Important Words

characteristic: a trait that is unique to a specific thing or person (*cognate: característica*)

compare: to show how things are alike or similar (*cognate: comparar*)

contrast: to show how things are different (*cognate: contrastar*)

Characteristics Characteristics are details that describe a person's personality, appearance, and actions in the text. Identifying characteristics can help you compare and contrast people and things.

Creative Thinking Characteristics
Has an open mind
Is curious
Good at brainstorming different ideas

Talk About It Discuss the activity with a partner or in a small group. Find two more characteristics of creative thinking from the article, "The Creative Connection." Then, think about which of the creative characteristics you are good at. Complete the sentence frames.

Creative thinkers also _____

and _____.

The creative characteristic I am best at is _____

_____

because _____

_____.

Extend Language Choose one of the inventors in the article. Use the sentence frames to describe three characteristics of the inventor.

The inventor I chose is _____.

He _____

_____

He also _____ and

_____

_____.

ELA R 2.7 Make reasonable assertions about a text through accurate, supporting citations. **(ELD R B8, B9, EI19, I9, EA9)**

Compare and Contrast You can organize information to help clarify what you are reading. Use the chart below to compare and contrast the characteristics of the two inventors in "The Creative Connection."

• Read the text to locate the details you will compare.
• How are they similar?

Philo Farnsworth	Ryan Patterson
Characteristic:	Characteristic:
Characteristic:	Characteristic:
Characteristic:	Characteristic:

Philo Farnsworth discovered his idea when plowing a potato field.

Extend Comprehension Use the chart below to compare and contrast the television and the translator glove. Use information about the inventors to fill in the chart.

Television	Translator Glove
Characteristic:	Characteristic:
Characteristic:	Characteristic:
Characteristic:	Characteristic:

ELA R 2.2 Analyze text that uses the compare-and-contrast organizational pattern.
(ELD R B8, B9, B11, B13, EI9, EI12, EI14, EA9)

Important Word

gerund phrase: a group of words that act as a gerund (*cognate: frase con gerundio*)

Gerund Phrases A gerund is the form of the verb ending in *-ing*. Gerunds act more like nouns than verbs. They can be the subject of a sentence. They can also be direct objects and objects of a preposition.

A gerund phrase is the gerund along with the adjective that modifies it or the objects of the action being expressed. Like gerunds, a gerund phrase can function like a noun in the sentence.

Gerund: Creative <u>thinking</u> has led to many famous inventions.

Gerund Phrase: <u>Creative thinking</u> has led to many famous inventions.

Creativity appears in different forms.

Extend Grammar In the sentences below, circle the gerund. Then, underline the gerund phrase.

1. Plowing a field gave one inventor the idea for television.

2. Standing in line gave another inventor an idea to help deaf people.

3. People use creative thinking to make unexpected connections.

4. A teenager's daydreaming led to the invention of TV.

5. Plowing a field is boring, so Philo Farnsworth fantasized about inventions.

6. Ryan Patterson loved creative experimenting.

7. Making a difference is almost as much fun as the inventing.

8. Improving old ideas is as important as creating new things.

9. Philo and Ryan were good at making connections.

10. Learning about teenage inventors is interesting.

ELA LC 1.0 Students write and speak with a command of standard English conventions appropriate to the grade level. **(ELD LC B8, EI11, I10, EA12)**

Connect to Writing

Compare and Contrast Paragraph How did you compare and contrast characteristics? Talk with a partner about what you learned.

On a separate sheet of paper, write a compare and contrast paragraph that answers the following questions:

- How are the inventors similar?
- How are the inventors different?

If you need help, use the sentence frames. The frames will help you organize your ideas.

The inventors are similar because _____

_____

and _____ .

However, they are different because _____

_____

_____ .

Anyone can be a creative thinker.

Connect to the Big Question Work with a partner. Find examples of greeting cards. They can be printed greeting cards or e-cards. Collect information about what greeting cards do. Decide whether you think greeting cards can help you communicate with other people. Then, share your research with the class.

Now, take some time to share your final ideas. Answer this question: How do we decide who we are? You can complete the sentence frame below. If you like, you can also choose another way to answer the question. Here are some choices: write a poem or write a short opinion essay.

We decide who we are by _____

_____ .

 ELA W 1.1 Choose the form of writing that best suits the intended purpose. **LS 2.3** Deliver oral responses to literature. **(ELD W B2, EI1, I3, I4, EA2, EA3; LS B1, B2, EI1, EI2, I3, I4, EA4, EA5)**

Vocabulary Review

Best Answer Read each sentence or question. Then, circle the best answer.

1. You should use the word "diverse" to describe
   A. things that are different from one another.
   B. the usual way to do something.
   C. beliefs or standards of behavior.
   D. things that are alike in some way.

2. A "custom" is
   A. when two things are alike.
   B. a message without words.
   C. a group of people in the same area.
   D. the usual way to do something.

3. What does "to respond" mean?
   A. to see
   B. to answer
   C. to believe
   D. to quote

4. People who are "unique" are
   A. special.
   B. verbal.
   C. similar.
   D. narrow.

· ·

Personal Response Complete a response for each sentence.

1. One of my ideals is _____
   _____.

2. My friends would describe my personality as _____
   _____.

3. From my perspective, challenges are _____
   _____.

4. I feel _____
   when I get a strong reaction from my friends.

5. My appearance is _____

   to me because _____.

ELA V 1.4 Monitor expository text for unknown words or words with novel meanings by using word, sentence, and paragraph clues to determine meaning. ELA V 1.5 Understand and explain "shades of meaning" in related words. (ELD V B1, B2, EI1, EI2, EI3, I1, I2, EA1, EA2)

Summarize A summary is a retelling of the main events or main ideas of the text. Read the passage below. Then, use the chart to help organize your summary.

Chris Gardner started life with high expectations, but sometimes life takes a different turn. He never expected to be a homeless single father, but it happened, and he found himself sitting in a public bathroom wondering what to do. That was the day he decided to turn his life around.

. . . .

Sequence Words Some sentences begin with sequence words that show the order of events in a story or article. Examples of sequence words are: *when, after, next, today, but,* and *then.*

Read the passage. Then, number these events in order.

Olivia is a very busy teenager. Every day after school she goes straight to choir practice. Then, her dad picks her up and takes her to soccer practice. Before going to drama rehearsal, she runs home to eat dinner. After drama, she does her homework.

_____ She eats dinner.   _____ She does her homework.

_____ Her dad picks her up.   _____ She goes to choir practice.

_____ She goes to soccer practice.   _____ She goes to drama rehearsal.

ELA R 2.3 Clarify an understanding of texts by creating outlines, logical notes, summaries, or reports. **(ELD R B9, B11, EI9, EI12, I10, EA9)**

Comprehension Review **167**

Important Words
....
alike

characteristic

compare

contrast

different

similar

Compare and Contrast When you show how things are alike or similar, you compare them. When you show how things are different, you contrast them.

Read the following sentences. Then, circle either Compare or Contrast.

1. Skateboarding is like snowboarding. Both are very dangerous.

    Compare   Contrast

2. Unlike team sports, skateboarders compete individually.

    Compare   Contrast

3. Both inventors have a creative thought process.

    Compare   Contrast

Venn diagram Read the paragraph. Then, complete the Venn diagram.

Anyone can be an inventor! Take Philo Farnsworth, for example. As a 14-year-old farm boy, he reflected on an idea, put it down on paper, and eventually it led to the development of today's television. Eighteen-year-old Ryan Patterson is another example. He observed people standing in line for fast food and thought of an idea to help people communicate. He built his invention and won an award. Both inventors showed that with a little creative thinking, anything can happen!

Philo Farnsworth   **Ryan Patterson**

ELA R 2.2 Analyze text that uses the compare-and-contrast organizational pattern.
(ELD R B8, B9, B11, EI9, EI12, EI14, EA9)

Grammar Review

Choose the Word Write the correct word on the line to complete the sentences.

> **Important Words**
> gerund
> gerund phrase
> object of the preposition
> preposition
> prepositional phrase

1. Andy loves _____. (skate/skating)

2. No matter how many times you fall, _____ again and again is important. (trying/try)

3. Ryan loves _____ experimenting. (create/creative)

4. I enjoy _____ machines. (inventing/invent)

5. _____ is my favorite hobby. (Daydream/Daydreaming)

- -

Complete the Sentence Complete each prepositional phrase to show where or when the activities described take place.

1. I like to eat in _____.

2. I saw something amazing at _____.

3. On _____ I got up early to make breakfast.

4. He hides his money under _____.

Trying again is important in becoming successful.

Write Sentences Write five new sentences using five prepositional phrases.

1. _____

2. _____

3. _____

4. _____

5. _____

ELA LC 1.0 Students write and speak with a command of standard English conventions appropriate to the grade level. **(ELD LC B8, EI9, EI11, EA12)**

How do we decide who we are?

In this unit, I read:

In this unit, I:

- learned new vocabulary words.
- read about different topics.
- used sequence words.
- infered the sequence of events.
- used compare and contrast words.
- used characteristics.
- learned how to summarize.
- learned how to compare and contrast things.

- learned about prepositions and prepositional phrases.
- learned about the objects of prepositions.
- learned about gerunds.
- learned about gerund phrases.
- wrote summary sentences.
- wrote a summary paragraph.
- wrote compare and contrast sentences.
- wrote a compare and contrast paragraph.

Reflection Think about what you learned in this unit. Complete each sentence frame. Share your answers with your teacher and classmates.

I wonder _____ .

I learned _____ .

I discovered _____ .

I still want to know _____ .

I still don't understand _____ .

THE BIG ?

How much do our communities shape us?

In this unit, I will read:

In this unit, I will:

- learn new vocabulary words.
- read about different topics.
- use cause and effect words.
- use *if/then* statements.
- use purpose words.
- make connections.
- learn about cause and effect.
- learn about setting a purpose for reading.
- learn about independent and subordinate clauses.
- learn about simple, compound, and complex sentences.
- learn about commas.
- learn about semicolons and colons.
- write cause and effect sentences.
- write a cause and effect paragraph.
- write a purpose for reading paragraph.
- write a make connections paragraph.

How much do our communities shape us?

Connect to the Big Question
Answer these questions. Discuss your answers with your teacher and classmates.

> What is your community like? How does your community shape who you are?

Extend the Big Question
Read each sentence frame. Write your opinions in each blank.

My community is
_____
_____
_____
_____
_____.

I take part in my community by
_____
_____
_____
_____
_____.

Discuss your opinions with your teacher and classmates.

 ELA LS 1.4 Select a focus, an organizational structure, and a point of view, matching the purpose, message, occasion, and vocal modulation to the audience. **ELA LS 1.7** Use effective rate, volume, pitch, and tone and align nonverbal elements to sustain audience interest and attention. **(ELD LS B1, B2, B3, EI1, EI2, EI3, I1, I2, I3, I4, EA1, EA2, EA3, EA4, EA5, EA6)**

How much do our communities shape us?

Big Question Words

Use your definitions from page 101 of the *Review and Assess* book.

belief

common
(cognate: *común*)

community
(cognate: *comunidad*)

connection
(cognate: *conexión*)

culture
(cognate: *cultura*)

family
(cognate: *familia*)

generation
(cognate: *generación*)

group
(cognate: *groupo*)

history
(cognate: *historia*)

influence
(cognate: *influencia*)

involve
(cognate: *involucrar*)

isolate

participation
(cognate: *participación*)

support

values
(cognate: *valores*)

Vocabulary Workshop

Guess The Word Read each clue. Then, fill in the line with the correct Big Question Word.

1. I happened in the past. I do not happen in the present.

   What am I? _____

2. We are a brother, a sister, a mother, and a grandfather.

   What are we? _____

3. We are not just one. There are many of us. We all live in the same place.

   What are we? _____

4. I am not unique. I am not special.

   What am I? _____

5. We are all 40 years old. We are a large group of people.

   What are we? _____

Personal Response Read each sentence. Then, fill in your response.

1. My community is _____
   _____.

2. I would like to involve myself in _____
   _____.

3. I think having values is _____
   because _____.

4. The best thing I like about my culture is _____
   _____.

5. I think it is important to support _____
   _____.

 ELA V 1.4 Monitor expository text for unknown words or words with novel meanings by using word, sentence, and paragraph clues to determine meaning. **ELA V 1.5** Understand and explain "shades of meaning" in related words. **(ELD V B1, B2, EI1, EI2, EI3, I1, I2, EA1, EA2)**

174 Vocabulary Workshop

Synonyms and Antonyms
Synonyms and antonyms can help you remember words and their meanings. A synonym is a word that means the same or almost the same as another word. An antonym is a word that means the opposite of another word.

Word Pairs Look at each pair of words. If the word pairs are synonyms, write an S. If the word pairs are antonyms, write an A.

1. connect, disconnect _____.
2. community, neighborhood _____.
3. observe, watch _____.
4. common, rare _____.
5. participate, join _____.

Complete the Sentences Use the words from the exercise above to fill in the blanks.

1. After I broke my ankle, I couldn't _____ in soccer.

2. Blake knows everyone in her _____, including Dr. Rivera, our principal Mr. Kurtz, and Judge Burns.

3. At our school, chalkboards are a _____ sight.

Write Sentences Select three Big Question Words and write a sentence for each that includes the word itself, its synonym, or its antonym. You can use a thesaurus or dictionary to help you.

_____

_____

_____

_____

ELA V 1.4 Monitor expository text for unknown words or words with novel meanings by using word, sentence, and paragraph clues to determine meaning. **(ELD V B1, B2, EI1, EI2, EI3, I1, I2, EA1, EA2)**

Vocabulary Workshop 175

Lesson 1
How much do our communities shape us?

Vocabulary

Important Words

community: a group of people living in the same place or share similiarities with each other (cognate: comunidad)

family: a group that is related or take care of each other (cognate: familia)

order: the way something is arranged; sequence (cognate: orden)

survey: a way to gather information by asking people questions and analyzing the results

values: the ideas you believe are important (cognate: valores)

Concept Words

benefits: positive things you receive (cognate: beneficios)

donate: to give your money or your time for a cause (cognate: donar)

volunteer: to offer your time or skills for free

Helping Others

Dialogue

Two teens are talking abut the effects of helping other people. Read the dialogue. Then, review the vocabulary words you read.

Teen 1: What are you doing after school? Do you want to do something.

Teen 2: Thanks for asking, but I can't do anything today. I am going to volunteer at a soup kitchen. You want to come?

Teen 1: No thanks. I have other plans. Seriously, how did you get stuck doing that?

Teen 2: I didn't get stuck. It's something I want to do. It's part of the values my family raised me with. When I donate my time to help others, I feel good.

Teen 1: So what do you do there?

Teen 2: I serve food to the homeless. It is part of my community service.

Teen 1: That sounds like work.

Teen 2: Well, if you want to experience the benefits of helping others, you have to do a little work. You also have to order your life so you have the time to volunteer. Surveys show that volunteering makes people feel good. So it is time well spent. You should try it!

Teen 1: Maybe I'll come after all.

Talk About It Discuss the question with a partner or in a small group. Why does helping others make people feel good? Complete the sentence frame.

Helping others makes people feel good because _____

_____.

_____.

_____.

Read the article. As you read, think about these questions:

- Why does helping others make people feel good?
- How does the topic of the article relate to the topic of the dialogue?

Help You, Help Me

Imagine you are in Oprah Winfrey's audience. She has just announced that every audience member will receive $1,000. Then, she asks you to use it to do something good for others. Would you be disappointed? Would you be excited?

The example above is a true story. The reason Oprah did it was to show her audience how good it feels to help others. The outcome was incredible. Her audience donated money to charities, helped family shelters, and started scholarship funds. They felt great because they helped others.

Oprah Winfrey gave $1,000 to each audience member to give away.

Scientists who study the benefits of helping call this the "helper's high." Through different surveys, scientists have learned that helping produces a positive reaction in the brain. People who volunteer in their community are healthier and happier. To get the "helper's high" you don't have to save the world! Just change the order of your life a little bit and act according to your beliefs and values. You'll feel the effects in large and small ways!

Talk About It Discuss the question with a partner or in a small group. If Oprah asked you to do something with a $1,000, what would you do? Complete the sentence frame.

I would _____

_____

_____.

ELA V 1.4 Monitor expository text for unknown words or words with novel meanings by using word, sentence, and paragraph clues to determine meaning. **(ELD V B2, B4, EI2, EI3, EI5, II, EA6) ELA R 2.3** Connect and clarify main ideas by identifying their relationships to other sources and related topics. **(ELD R B8, B11, EI9, I10, EA9)**

Language Workshop

 FORM & FUNCTION

Important Words
. . . .

cause: the reason why something happens (*cognate: causa*)

effect: what happens next after something happens; the result (*cognate: efecto*)

Cause and Effect Words The article you just read talked about the causes and effects of helping others.

A cause is an event, action, or feeling that produces a result.	An effect is what happens as a result of a cause.

This chart shows some words you can use to identify examples of cause and effect. Read the chart. Circle the words that appear in the article, "Help You, Help Me."

Cause words	Effect words
because	as a result
produce	so
since	consequence
cause	effect
reason	outcome

. . . .

Talk About It Discuss the activity with a partner or in a small group. Decide if each sentence is describing a cause or an effect. Then, use words from the chart to complete the sentences.

1. _____ of volunteering, many people feel great.

2. _____ Oprah Winfrey gave her audience members $1,000 each, the _____ has been very positive.

3. Scientists believe volunteering can _____ a "helper's high."

Extend Language Now create a cause and effect sentence of your own. Use information from the chart and the article.

_____

_____

_____

_____

ELA V 1.4 Monitor expository text for unknown words or words with novel meanings by using word, sentence, and paragraph clues to determine meaning. **(ELD V B4, EI3, EI4, EI5, I4, I7, EA3, EA6)**

Comprehension Workshop

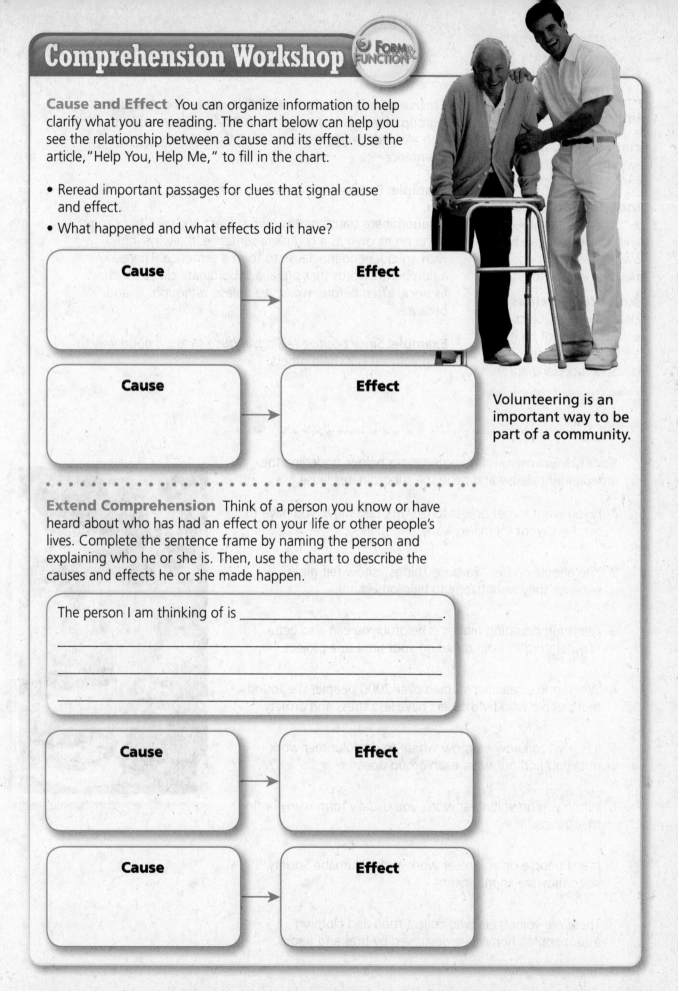

FORM & FUNCTION

Cause and Effect You can organize information to help clarify what you are reading. The chart below can help you see the relationship between a cause and its effect. Use the article, "Help You, Help Me," to fill in the chart.

- Reread important passages for clues that signal cause and effect.
- What happened and what effects did it have?

Cause		Effect
	→	

Cause		Effect
	→	

Volunteering is an important way to be part of a community.

Extend Comprehension Think of a person you know or have heard about who has had an effect on your life or other people's lives. Complete the sentence frame by naming the person and explaining who he or she is. Then, use the chart to describe the causes and effects he or she made happen.

The person I am thinking of is _____.

_____

_____

Cause		Effect
	→	

Cause		Effect
	→	

ELA R 2.7 Make reasonable assertions about a text through accurate, supporting citations. (ELD R B9, B11, B14, EI9, EI13, I10, EA9)

Grammar

Important Words

clause: a group of words with its own subject and verb (cognate: *cláusula*)

independent clause: a clause with a subject and a verb that can be its own sentence (cognate: *cláusula independiente*)

subordinate clause: a clause with a subject and a verb that cannot be its own sentence (cognate: *cláusula independiente*)

Clauses: Independent and Subordinate A clause is a group of words in a sentence that has its own subject and verb. An independent clause is one that can stand by itself as a sentence.

Example: Positive feelings reduce stress.

A subordinate clause has its own subject and verb but cannot stand on its own as a complete sentence. It always joins with an independent clause to form a sentence. There are a number of words that signal a subordinate clause, such as *since, after, before, while, as, unless, although, if,* and *because.*

Example: *Since positive feelings reduce stress,* a good way to help yourself is to help others.

Extend Grammar In the sentences below, underline the independent clause and circle the subordinate clause.

1. If you want to get tickets to Oprah's talk show, you have to send away for them very early.

2. The people on her "Favorite Things" show felt great because they were happy to help others.

3. Although donating money is helpful, you can also get a "helper's high" from donating your time to a project.

4. When one researcher studied over 2000 people, she found that people who help others have less stress and anxiety.

5. It is hard to know to know where to do volunteer work until you find out what each group does.

6. When you do volunteer work, you usually form many lasting friendships.

7. Many people do volunteer work at the Humane Society, since they are animal lovers.

8. There are volunteers who collect food and clothing after people's homes are destroyed by fires and floods.

ELA LC 1.1 Use simple, compound, and compound-complex sentences; use effective coordination and subordination of ideas to thoughts. **(ELD LC B8, EI11, I11, EA12)**

Connect to Writing

Cause and Effect Sentences How did you learn to identify cause and effect? Talk with a partner about what you learned.

On a separate sheet of paper, write cause and effect sentences that answer the following questions:

• What causes people to help others?

• What are some effects of helping others?

If you need help, use the sentence frames.

People help others because _____

_____.

For example, _____

_____.

As a result of helping others, many people feel _____

_____.

> **Writing Tips**
> Don't forget to
> 1. use cause and effect words.
> 2. use a diagram to help organize your ideas.
> 3. go back and revise your writing.

Former President Jimmy Carter donates much of his time to helping others.

Tell a Story Work with a partner. Tell a story about a character who helps other people. What does the character do to help people? Why do the people need the character's help? After you practice telling the story with your partner, share your story with other classmates.

Tips for Your Story

• Give names to your characters.

• Think of the story's events. Also, give your story a setting, or a place where the story takes place

• Use your voice correctly as you tell the story. Change your expressions to keep your listeners interested in what you are saying.

ELA LS 1.2 Identify the tone, mood, and emotion conveyed in the oral communication. **ELA LS 1.7** Use effective rate, volume, pitch, and tone and align nonverbal elements to sustain audience interest and attention. **ELA LS 2.1** Deliver narrative presentations. **(ELD LS B1, B2, EI1, I2, I3, EA1, EA2, EA3, EA5)**

Lesson 2
How much do our communities shape us?

Vocabulary

Important Words

generation: a group of people who are about the same age *(cognate: generación)*

influence: the effect that someone or something has on you *(cognate: influencia)*

involve: to include or be part of something

judge: to make a decision or opinion based on facts *(cognate: juzgar)*

support: to provide evidence for something

Concept Words

focus: to concentrate on one thing; to look closely at *(cognate: enfocar)*

mentor: an adult who guides a younger person toward success *(cognate: mentor)*

sponsor: to support something or someone with your time or money

Community Members

Dialogue

The teacher and students are talking about mentors. Read the dialogue. Then, review the vocabulary words you read.

Teacher:	Today we're talking about mentors. Does anyone have someone they look up to?
Student 1:	I look up to my grandpa. He is really involved in my life.
Teacher:	That's great. You are lucky to have someone of his generation to share his wisdom and support you. What other kinds of positive influences do people have in their lives?
Student 2:	I have a tutor who sponsors my reading program and helps me focus on my studies.
Teacher:	That's another great example of a community member acting as a mentor. Anyone else?
Student 3:	I have one. I met my mentor last year when I was in trouble and making bad choices. He judges what each kid in the program needs. He helped me learn to make better decisions when it came to picking my friends. I'm really lucky he came along.

Talk About It Discuss the questions with a partner or a small group. Think about someone you look up to. Why is he or she a good role model? Complete the sentence frame.

_____ is a good role model

for me because _____

_____.

Read the article. As you read, think about these questions:

• What makes a good mentor? What impact do mentors have?
• How does the topic of the article relate to the topic of the dialogue?

Mentors Make a Difference

Most kids see their parents as mentors.

Do you have a mentor? A mentor is someone who has a good influence on your life. A mentor supports you, and helps you judge right from wrong. You may have talent and energy, but you can't do it alone.

In a recent survey, kids saw parents as their most important mentors. If parents are involved in their daily lives, they have the most impact as role models.

Next on the list were teachers. One teacher in Los Angeles, named Mr. Ramos, expects his students to come to school two hours early and stay two hours late. If the students are willing to work hard, Mr. Ramos helps them focus on how to get into college.

For many young people, the community plays an important role. Many community groups sponsor programs that teach skills to young people. These programs often need more volunteers. If more people from different generations would volunteer, teens would have more mentors and learn more life skills.

Talk About It Discuss the activity with a partner or in a small group. How do mentors make a difference to young people? Complete the sentence frame.

Mentors make a difference by _____

_____.

ELA V 1.4 Monitor expository text for unknown words or words with novel meanings by using word, sentence, and paragraph clues to determine meaning. **(ELD V B2, B4, EI2, EI3, EI5, I1, I5, EA3) ELA R 2.3** Connect and clarify main ideas by identifying their relationships to other sources and related topics. **(ELD R B8, B9, EI9, EI12, I9, I10, EA9) Reading 183**

Form & Function

Important Words

cause: the reason why something happens; a reason *(cognate: causa)*

effect: what happens next after something happens; the result *(cognate: efecto)*

relationship: the connection between two things *(cognate: relación)*

If/Then Statements You can identify cause and effect relationships in the text by looking for *if/then* statements.

If people volunteer	*(then)* they make a difference to kids.
If teens work hard	*(then)* they succeed.

The first part of the above sentences describe the *cause*, and the second part of the sentences describe the consequence, or *effect*. The word *then* will not always appear, but it is still implied by the way the sentence is written. For example, read the following sentence: If more kids had mentors, they would do better in school. This sentence doesn't use the word *then*, but it is implied.

Talk About It Discuss the questions with a partner or in a small group. Find two *if/then* sentences in the article, "Mentors Make a Difference." Fill in the sentence frames.

1. If _____ ,
   _____

   then, _____

   _____ .

2. If _____ ,
   _____

   then, _____

   _____ .

Extend Language Now create your own *if/then* sentence based on information in the article. Make sure it shows a cause and effect. Use the sentence frame.

If _____ ,

_____

then, _____

_____ .

ELA R 2.7 Make reasonable assertions about a text through accurate, supporting citations. **(ELD R B9, B11, B14, EI9, EI13, I10, EA9)**

Comprehension Workshop

Cause and Effect Cause and effect relationships explain connections between events. Often one cause will lead to a chain of events. Use information from the article, "Mentors Make a Difference," to fill in the chart below. Answer the questions below before you begin. The first cause is already filled in for you.

- How do *if/then* statements give clues to cause and effect?
- How can one cause lead to a chain of events?

Cause
Mr. Ramos mentors the students

↓

Effect/Cause

↓

Effect/Cause

↓

Effect

Some teachers go the extra mile for students.

Extend Comprehension Think of someone you that you have had an effect on. Complete the sentence frame. Then, fill in the chart.

I affected _____

by _____.

Cause

Effect   **Effect**

🐻 **ELA R 2.4** Clarify an understanding of texts by creating outlines, logical notes, summaries, or reports. **(ELD R B9, B11, B14, EI9, EI13, I10, EA9)**

Grammar

Important Words

compound sentence: a sentence with two or more independent clauses (*cognate: oración compuesta*)

simple sentence: a statement with a single independent clause (*cognate: oración simple*)

cómplex sentence: a sentence with one independent clause and one or more subordinate clauses (*cognate: oración compleja*)

Simple, Compound, and Complex Sentences

Sentences can be classified according to the number of clauses they contain. A clause is a group of words with its own subject and verb.

A simple sentence contains one independent clause. Standing alone, the independent clause is a complete sentence.

Example: Young people often need help.

A compound sentence contains two or more independent clauses and is usually linked by commas and conjunctions like *and* or *but*. A compound sentence is two or more complete sentences linked together.

Example: Young people often need help, and mentors are here to help out.

A complex sentence contains an independent clause, plus at least one subordinate clause that only makes sense as part of the bigger sentence.

Example: Because young people often need help, mentors are here to help out. (The subordinate clause is "Because young people often need help,")

- -

Extend Grammar Label each sentence below as either 1= simple, 2= compound, or 3= complex. Underline the independent clauses, and circle the subordinate clauses.

1. All great adventure heroes have one thing in common. ____

2. You have lots of talent, and your friends support you. ____

3. The original mentor was a character in *The Odyssey*. ____

4. Mentor was the wise teacher of the hero's teen son. ____

5. When one recent survey asked kids who they looked up to, kids judged parents as their most important mentors. ____

6. Teachers ranked second in that survey because they can guide and challenge young people. ____

7. Some kids in Mr. Ramos's class don't want to go to college, but most of his students are college bound. ____

8. Many adults volunteer as tutors. ____

ELA LC 1.1 Use simple, compound, and compound-complex sentences; use effective coordination and subordination of ideas to express thoughts **(ELD LC B8, EI11, I11, EA12)**

Connect to Writing

Cause and Effect Paragraph How did you find *if/then* statements and cause and effect statements in what you read? Talk with a partner about what you learned.

On a separate sheet of paper, write a cause and effect paragraph about Mr. Ramos and his students. Answer the following questions:

• How do mentors effect changes in kids?
• What were the effects?

If you need help, use the sentence frames.

_____ caused several different

effects on _____.

His students came two hours early to school, therefore _____

_____.

He told his students that if _____

he would _____.

If I were in Mr. Ramos' class, then _____

_____.

Different generations can share their wisdom.

Research Communities Work with a partner. Discuss the power of community and working together. Look for information to help you learn more. Explain why the power of community is important. Then, share your research with the class.

Tips for Your Research

• Think of questions you would want to answer. How does the power of community help people in that community?

• Use different sources to find information about your role model. You can use magazines, newspapers, or Internet sources. These sources can help you support your opinions with information.

• Organize your information. Make sure your main ideas are clear. This will help your audience understand what you are saying.

ELA LS 1.4 Select a focus, an organizational structure, and a point of view, matching the purpose, message, occasion, and vocal modulation to the audience. **ELA LS 1.5** Emphasize salient points to assist the listener in following the main ideas and concepts. **ELA LS 2.2** Deliver informative presentations. **(ELD LS B1, B2, B3, EI1, EI2, EI4, EI6, I1, I3, I4, I6, EA3, EA4, EA5, EA8)**

Lesson 3
How much do our communities shape us?

Vocabulary

Important Words

belief: an important idea or opinion that you think is true

connection: a link between two things, people or ideas
(*cognate: conexión*)

participation: taking part in something with others
(*cognate: participación*)

prepare: to get ready for something before it happens
(*cognate: preparar*)

support: to provide evidence for something

Concept Words

caution: a warning to be careful

reward: a gift, like money, that you receive for doing something

self-esteem: a feeling of pride in yourself
(*cognate: autoestima*)

Rewards and Pride

Dialogue

Two teens are talking about the benefits and drawbacks of rewards. Read the dialogue. Then, review the vocabulary words you read.

Teen 1: Hey, I got a reward for good attendance!

Teen 2: What was the reward?

Teen 1: A new cell phone with lots of free minutes! All I had to do was come to school every day!

Teen 2: It's cool that the community supports kids, but they should do it with caution when it comes to prizes. Last year my participation in school events was higher. I also studied more because I wanted to be rewarded for getting higher grades. I did my best but didn't get a prize. I learned there isn't always a connection between hard work and prizes.

Teen 1: Did it hurt your self-esteem not to get a prize?

Teen 2: A little bit. It also changed my belief in rewards. They don't always prepare you for the real world. Do you think your future boss will give you a prize for coming to work every day? Just like adults, kids need to learn to take pride in themselves and the hard work they put into something. Prizes are nice, but self-esteem is better.

Talk About It Discuss the questions with a partner or in a small group. If you could win a cell phone for perfect attendance, would it motivate you to come to school every day? Why or why not? Circle your opinion. Then, complete the sentence frame.

The reward (would/would not) motivate me because

_____

_____

Reading

Read the article. As you read, think about these questions:

- Why do communities give rewards to students?
- How does the topic of the article relate to the topic of the dialogue?

Seeking Student Success

Some rewards make a big difference to students.

What if you got paid for getting passing grades? Would it make you study harder? What if you got a new cell phone, just for coming to school every day? Rewards like these are becoming more common in schools today. Communities are paying kids for higher grades and more participation in school activities, in the belief that rewards support student self-esteem. Is this connection really true?

Rewards make a big difference to some kids. In the Chicago area, Gilberto Roman received an award and said, "It was the most important factor in me applying to college."

Some educators, however, are against the use of rewards and say to use them with caution. They argue that rewards don't really change the behavior of most kids. They also say some rewards are too competitive, so that even students who are doing their best are not rewarded. Many believe rewards don't prepare students for the real world, where the best motivation comes from taking pride in your work.

Talk About It Discuss the questions with a partner or in a small group. What do you think about rewards? Are they helpful or harmful to student success? Why? Use the sentence frame.

I think _____

because _____

_____

 ELA V 1.4 Monitor expository text for unknown words or words with novel meanings by using word, sentence, and paragraph clues to determine meaning. **(ELD V B2, B4, EI5, I1, EA1) ELA R 2.3** Connect and clarify main ideas by identifying their relationships to other sources and related topics. **(ELD R B8, EI9, I9, EA9)**

Language Workshop

Important Words

preview: to look closely at a text before you read *(cognate: entretener)*

establish: to identify or set *(cognate: establecer)*

purpose: reason/ intention; plan *(cognate: persuadir)*

Purpose Words The purpose for reading is the reason why you read a text. To establish a purpose for reading, it helps to preview the article or story. It will help you focus your reading.

Preview the Article By
Reading the title
Looking at the pictures
Reading the beginnings of paragraphs

Use details from the article on page 189 to complete the sentence frames.

The title is _____.

The picture shows _____.

The beginnings of the paragraphs talk about things such as

_____

_____

_____

Talk About It Discuss the question with a partner or in a small group. Talk about some of the other places you see previews. For example, you see previews of new movies and television shows. How are they like the previews you are doing in this lesson? Complete the sentence frame.

Previews of new movies and television shows are like the

previews we are reading because _____

_____.

Extend Language Now think about the information you found while previewing "Seeking Student Success." What does it tell you about the article? Complete the sentence frame.

The details tell me the article is about _____

_____

_____.

ELA R 2.7 Make reasonable assertions about a text through accurate, supporting citations. **(ELD R B9, B11, EI9, I10, EA9)**

Comprehension Workshop

Purpose for Reading Look back at the information you gathered when you previewed "Seeking Student Success," on page 190. Then, fill in the shortened version of the "Preview of Article" chart. Choose one of the purposes for reading that are listed below. Put a check (✓) by it. Then, complete the sentence frame.

Preview of Article

Title:

What is the article about?

Purposes for Reading	
To learn about a subject:	
To gain understanding:	
To take an action:	
To read for enjoyment:	

I chose _____ as a purpose for reading

because _____.

Some students try their best but still don't receive awards.

Extend Comprehension Find a newspaper or magazine article. Preview the article. Then, fill in the chart. Use the information to set your purpose for reading.

Preview of Article

Title:

Pictures:

Beginnings of paragraphs:

What is the article about?

Purpose for Reading

ELA R 2.4 Clarify an understanding of texts by creating outlines, logical notes, summaries, or reports. **(ELD R B8, B9, B11, EI9, EI12, I10, EA9)**

Grammar

Important Words

comma: a punctuation mark used to separate words or groups of words *(cognate: coma)*

Punctuation: Commas A comma is a punctuation mark used to separate words or groups of words in a sentence. Commas show readers where to pause. They also help prevent confusion and make sentences easier to read.

Commas separate words in a series:

Example: In the case of Jacob, Danielle, Zach, Louisa, and many others, the rewards came from a larger community.

Commas separate phrases in a series:

Example: Students do good work, earn rewards, and experience higher self-esteem.

Commas also indicate a pause before and after adverbs like *however, meanwhile,* and *though.*

Example: Students will go back to doing poorly, however, if they don't win every time.

Extend Grammar Read the sentences below. Add commas where necessary.

1. Parents teachers and city leaders disagree on when and how to reward students.

2. Danielle just got a new cell phone Zach drove off in a new car and Louisa was promised $500 in college money.

3. In the Chicago area leaders wanted to raise the rates of high school graduation for Hispanic teens.

4. A number of educators and community leaders disagree with such rewards however.

5. Students who participate for external rewards like money cars and cell phones don't really learn about real life.

6. Some students aren't able to improve their test scores though no matter how many TVs or cars you dangle in front of them.

7. Many experts believe however that the best motivation is intrinsic.

8. That kind of pride some say lasts longer than anything money can buy.

ELA LC 1.3 Use colons after the salutation in business letters, semicolons to connect independent clauses, and commas when linking two clauses with a conjunction in compound sentences. **(ELD LC B7, B8, B9, EI9, EI11 I11, EA12)**

Connect to Writing

Writing Tips
Don't forget to
1. think about why you preview a text.
2. think about different purposes for reading.
3. go back and revise your writing.

Purpose for Reading Paragraph Think of all you have learned in this lesson. What new words did you use? How did you learn to set your purpose for reading? Talk with a partner about what you learned.

On a separate sheet of paper, write a paragraph that answers the following questions:

• How did you preview text to set a purpose?
• How did you decide your purpose for reading?
• What was your purpose for reading?

If you need help getting started, use the sentence frames.

I previewed the text by looking at _____
_____
_____

Then, I decided my purpose for reading by _____
_____
_____.

My purpose for reading was _____
_____
_____.

Some say the best motivation comes from your own pride.

Write an Essay On a separate sheet of paper or on a computer, write an essay about rewards. Should schools give rewards to students? What do you think? Try to persuade your readers.

Tips for Your Essay

• State your opinions clearly. Use words to persuade your readers.

• Support your opinions with facts and other evidence. Search the Internet to find information about your topic.

• Try to include other opinions that you don't agree with and explain why. The article you read on page 189 can provide some examples.

• Use the Writing Process Handbook at the end of this book. This will help you with drafting and revising. If you are writing on a computer, use spell-check and remember to follow the directions for how to use a word-processing program.

ELA W 1.2 Create multiple-paragraph expository compositions. **ELA W 1.4** Use organizational features of electronic text to locate information. **ELA W 2.5** Write persuasive compositions. **(ELD W B2, EI2, EI3, EI4, I2, I3, I8, EA6, EA8)**

Connect to Writing **193**

Lesson 4
How much do our communities shape us?

Vocabulary

Important Words

always: all the time

connection: a link between two things, people or ideas (*cognate: conexión*)

family: a group of people who are related and take care of each other (*cognate: familia*)

influence: the effect that someone or something has on you (*cognate: influencia*)

values: the ideas you believe are important (*cognate: valores*)

Concept Words

advertiser: someone who makes ads, like TV commercials

brand loyalty: when you buy or use the same product all the time

marketing: promoting and selling products (*cognate: mercadeo*)

Commercialism

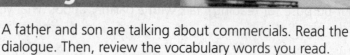

Dialogue

A father and son are talking about commercials. Read the dialogue. Then, review the vocabulary words you read.

Son:	Hey dad, I saw a commercial for some shoes I really want. Can we go shopping?
Father:	Well, you know our family can't afford expensive things. Are these shoes something you really need, or is the flashy marketing the biggest influence on your decision?
Son:	You always ask that. I just want the shoes because they're cool.
Father:	That's exactly what advertisers want. Those commercials make a connection between what they're selling and what's "cool."
Son:	Kids aren't stupid. We know what's cool and what's not.
Father:	Do you think the advertisers don't know that? They watch your every move. Then, they create commercials that tap teen values so they get your brand loyalty.
Son:	Come on, Dad! The shoes are cheap.
Father:	That depends on your definition of cheap.

Talk About It Discuss the questions with a partner or in a small group. How do you decide what is "cool"? Who or what influences your buying decisions? Use the sentence frame.

My buying decisions are influenced most by _____

and _____

_____

Read the article. As you read, think about these questions:

- How do advertisers get brand loyalty?
- What examples of propaganda are in the article?

BUYING POWER

Teens in the U.S. have a buying power of $300 billion a year.

What's your favorite brand of clothing, soft drink, or MP3 player? Most kids can name these off the top of their heads. This is called brand loyalty, and it is why the marketing industry cares so much about teens.

Teens have an incredible influence over family purchases. Advertisers want to be on your list of favorites so you will always buy their products. To get there, they stick brand names in movies, TV shows, video games, and Internet films you watch everyday. They try to tell you what to eat, wear, and listen to. They want to make sure you draw a connection between their products and what's "cool."

You might say "I'm too smart to be fooled," but it's hard to go against what is "popular." You can beat the advertisers by being on guard against hidden messages. Buy products based on your needs and values, not what's popular. Use your buying power to say "no thanks."

Talk About It Review the article with a partner or in a small group. What examples of propaganda are in the article? Use the sentence frame to give an example.

One example of propaganda in the article is _____
_____
_____.

ELA V 1.4 Monitor expository text for unknown words or words with novel meanings by using word, sentence, and paragraph clues to determine meaning. **(ELD V B2, B4, EI5, I1, EA1) ELA R 2.8** Note instances of unsupported inferences, fallacious reasoning, persuasion, and propaganda in text. **(ELD R B8, EI9, I9, EA9)**

FORM & FUNCTION

Important Words

connect: to link or join together (*cognate: evento*)

experience: knowledge you gain as you do something often (*cognate: experiencia*)

Make Connections Establishing a purpose for reading helps you focus your reading. One purpose you can set for all your reading is to make connections between an article or story and your own experiences.

To make connections to the article, "Buying Power," ask yourself: Does the article apply to my life? Circle your opinion. Then, complete the sentence frame to answer the question.

The article, "Buying Power" (does/ does not) apply to my life

because _____

_____

_____

_____.

Talk About It: Discuss the activity with a partner or in a small group. Talk about all the people and products you are loyal to. Why do you think people become loyal to a certain brand of clothes or soft drink? Is it really important? Complete the sentence frame.

I think people become loyal to certain products because _____

_____

_____

_____.

Extend Language Make a connection to the following question: "Does the article give advice I can use?" Circle your opinion. Then, complete the sentence frames.

The article (does/ does not) give advice I can use. For example,

_____

_____

_____

_____.

ELA R 2.7 Make reasonable assertions about a text through accurate, supporting citations. **(ELD R B9, B11, EI9, I10, EA9)**

Comprehension Workshop

FORM & FUNCTION

Set a Purpose for Reading When you make connections between what you read and your own experiences, it helps you decide your purpose for reading.

Use the article, "Buying Power," to fill details into the chart below that connect to your experiences.

Details from the text	Connection to my experiences

Advertisers keep a close eye on teens.

Now choose a purpose for reading. Put a check mark (✓) next to it. Then, complete the sentence frame.

Purposes for Reading	
To learn about a subject:	
To gain understanding:	
To take an action:	
To read for enjoyment:	

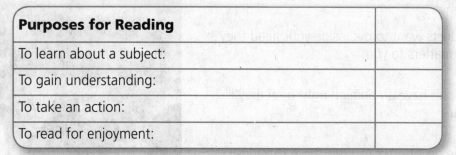

I chose _____ as a purpose for reading

because _____ .

Extend Comprehension Find a newspaper or magazine article. Use the chart to make connections to the article and set your purpose for reading.

Details from the text	Connection to my experiences
My purpose for reading	

![bear logo] **ELA R 2.4** Clarify an understanding of texts by creating outlines, logical notes, summaries, or reports. **ELA R 2.1** Identify the structural features of popular media and use the features to obtain information. **(ELD R B8, B9, B10, B11, EI9, EI12, I13, EI14, EA9)**

Grammar

Important Words

colon: a punctuation mark (:) used after an independent clause for lists, time, a business letter, or on warnings and labels

semicolon: a punctuation mark (;) which connects two independent clauses that are closely connected in meaning

Punctuation: Semicolons and Colons A semicolon connects two independent clauses that are closely related. The clauses could be separated by a period, making them sentences, but a semicolon signals that the clauses are connected in meaning.

Example: Don't underestimate your influence; the money kids spend helps drive the American economy.

Colons are used after an independent clause to introduce a list of items.

Example: Teens use their income on items they both need and want: clothes, food, video games, school supplies, and movies.

Extend Grammar Read the sentences below. Add colons or semicolons where needed.

1. People who sell products want to get inside your head they want to know what matters to you.

2. Don't worry if you don't have an opinion right now they'll make one up for you.

3. "Brand loyalty" is the devotion consumers have to various products food, detergents, electronics, medicines, and toiletries.

4. Advertisers target teens for one reason teens are open to developing what's called "brand loyalty."

5. Consumers influence buying choices by talking to others around them friends, family members, and co-workers.

6. Think about it brand loyalty is strong if you can probably name your favorite brands of soft drinks and electronics right off the top of your head.

7. Kids like you decide what's cool, and what's not cool don't think advertisers aren't watching your every move.

8. Advertisers use various media to deliver a sales pitch movies, TV, radio, magazines, newspapers, and Internet pop-ups.

ELA LC 1.3 Use colons after the salutation in business letters, semicolons to connect independent clauses, and commas when linking two clauses with a conjunction in compound sentences. (ELD LC B7, B8, B9, EI9, EI11 I11, EA12)

Connect to Writing

Writing Tips
Don't forget to
1. think about questions that help you make connections.
2. think about different purposes for reading.
3. go back and revise your writing.

Make Connections Paragraph How did you learn to make connections and set your purpose for reading? Talk with a partner about what you learned.

On a separate sheet of paper, write a paragraph that answers the following questions:

- How did you make connections?
- How did you set your purpose for reading?
- What was your purpose for reading?

If you need help getting started, use the sentence frames.

I made connections by _____

_____.

Then, I decided my purpose for reading by _____

_____

My purpose for reading was _____

_____.

You can beat the advertisers by becoming a better educated consumer.

Connect to the Big Question Think about all the articles you read in this unit. What article did you like best? What article did you not like? Then, talk about your favorite article and say what the article was about.

Now, take some time to share your final ideas. Answer this question: How much do our communities shape us? You can complete the sentence frame below.

Our communities shape us by _____

_____

_____

ELA W 2.4 Write responses to literature. **LS 2.3** Deliver oral responses to literature. **(ELD W B2, EI1, I3, I4, EA2, EA3; LS B1, B2, EI1, EI2, I3, I4, EA4, EA5)**

How much do our communities shape us?

Big Question Words and Important Words
. . . .

always

belief

common

community

connection

culture

family

generation

group

history

influence

involve

isolate

judge

order

participation

support

survey

values

Vocabulary Review

Same Meaning Read the sentences. Fill in the blank with another word that means the same as the vocabulary word.

1. I tried to <u>influence</u> my sister's decision.

   I tried to _____ my sister's decision.

2. The <u>connection</u> between us is strong.

   The _____ between us is strong.

3. She has very strong <u>beliefs</u>.

   She has very strong _____.

4. I tried to be fair by <u>involving</u> everyone in my class.

   I tried to be fair by _____ everyone.

5. Her concerns are very <u>common</u>.

   Her concerns are very _____.

Write Sentences Write a sentence using the words below.

1. culture _____

   _____.

2. history _____

   _____.

3. judge _____

4. prepare _____

   _____.

5. support _____

   _____.

ELA V 1.4 Monitor expository text for unknown words or words with novel meanings by using word, sentence, and paragraph clues to determine meaning. **ELA V 1.5** Understand and explain "shades of meaning" in related words. **(ELD V B1, B2, EI1, EI2, EI3, I1, I2, EA1, EA2)**

Cause and Effect A cause is an event, action, or feeling that produces a result. An effect is what happens as a result of the cause. Read the following sentences. Then, write the cause and effect.

1. Because of Oprah's generosity, her audience got to experience the joy of giving.

   Cause: _____

   Effect: _____

2. Scientists have found that helping others produces a "helper's high."

   Cause: _____

   Effect: _____

3. When mentors spend extra time with kids, the kids learn skills to succeed in life.

   Cause: _____

   Effect: _____

Complete the Chart Read the paragraph. Then, complete the chart.

Marley struggled in school because she needed more help with homework. Her teacher noticed, and suggested she go to the tutoring center. She was nervous but went anyway, hoping it would help her grades. There, she met Mr. Hutchins, who started working with her every day after school. Soon, Marley's grades improved.

Mentors can make a big difference to kids.

Cause	Effect/Cause	Effect/Cause	Effect

ELA R 2.7 Make reasonable assertions about a text through accurate, supporting citations.
(ELD R B9, B11, B14, EI9, EI13, I10, EA9)

Comprehension Review

Important Words
....
connect

establish

experience

preview

purpose

Purpose for Reading Your purpose for reading is the reason you read a text. You can establish your purpose by connecting the literature to your own experiences.

Read the titles. Then, answer the questions.

1. Title: "How Teenagers Can Manage Their Money"
   How does this topic apply to your life?

   _____.

   What might be your purpose for reading it?

   _____.

2. Title: "The Latest in Celebrity Gossip"
   Why might this topic be interesting?

   _____.

   What might be your purpose for reading it?

   _____.

3. Title "Great Leaders in U.S. History"
   How does this topic apply to your life?

   _____.

   What might be your purpose for reading it?

   _____.

There are many different purposes for reading.

Best Purpose Read the examples below. Then, select the best purpose for reading.

1. Bayla is reading a newspaper article about world leaders. She is doing a report for school.
   - A. to gather information
   - B. for entertainment
   - C. to take an action
   - D. to gain understanding

2. Maurice is reading a magazine article about his favorite skateboarder.
   - A. to take action
   - B. to gather information
   - C. for entertainment
   - D. to learn about culture

3. Lily is reading her bicycle manual so she can fix her gears.
   - A. to learn about culture
   - B. for entertainment
   - C. to write a report
   - D. to take action

ELA R 2.3 Connect and clarify main ideas by identifying their relationships to other sources and related topics. **(ELD R B9, B11, EI9, I10, EA9)**

Choose the Word Choose the correct word for each sentence.

1. Getting tickets to that show is difficult
   _____ it is so popular. (because/that)

2. _____ one researcher studied hundreds
   of people, she found many folks who enjoyed helping others.
   (As/When)

3. _____ one recent survey asked kids
   who they admire, kids said their parents. (Because/When)

4. Teachers are also popular with kids
   _____ they can guide young people.
   (because/while)

Important Words
. . . .
- clause
- colon
- comma
- complex sentence
- compound sentence
- independent clause
- semicolon
- simple sentence
- subordinate clause

Punctuation Use commas, colons, and semicolons to punctuate
the following sentences. Write the new sentence on the lines.

1. One girl bought a new cell phone another got a car and many
   others got cash.

   _____

   _____

2. Teenagers use the money they earn to buy all sorts of things
   new clothes sports equipment fast food and jewelry.

   _____

   _____

3. Advertisers love teenagers for one reason teenagers have more
   money to spend these days.

   _____

   _____

4. My favorite things are my MP3 player my video game and
   my blue baseball cap.

   _____

   _____

ELA LC 1.3 Use colons after the salutation in business letters, semicolons to connect independent clauses, and
commas when linking two clauses with a conjunction in compound sentences. **(ELD LC B7, B8, B9, EI9, EI11 I11,
EA12)**

How much do our communities shape us?

In this unit, I read:

In this unit, I:

- learned new vocabulary words.
- read about different topics.
- used cause and effect words.
- used *if/then* statements.
- used purpose words.
- made connections.
- learned about cause and effect.
- learned about setting a purpose for reading.

- learned about independent and subordinate clauses.
- learned about simple, compound, and complex sentences.
- learned about commas.
- learned about semicolons and colons.
- wrote cause and effect sentences.
- wrote a cause and effect paragraph.
- wrote a purpose for reading paragraph.
- wrote a make connections paragraph.

Reflection Think about what you learned in this unit. Complete each sentence frame. Share your answers with your teacher and classmates.

I wonder _____.

I learned _____.

I discovered _____.

I still want to know _____.

I still don't understand _____.

Table of Contents

The Writing Process

You write every day. You may have e-mailed a friend. You may have made a list of all the things you need to do today. You may have worked on a school assignment. These are all forms of writing. Now it is time to move on to a bigger writing project.

Use the information about the writing process in this handbook to write an essay or story. The writing process takes you step by step from choosing a topic, to publishing, or presenting, what you have written.

The Writing Process

Use these five steps to write your essay.

1 Prewriting Brainstorm topic ideas, choose a topic, do research, and organize details before you begin writing.

2 Drafting Write your ideas down on paper in roughly the way you planned.

3 Revising Read your first draft and look to find ways you can make it better or more interesting. Then, you revise it. Revise means to make changes.

4 Editing and Proofreading Correct errors in grammar, spelling, and mechanics.

5 Publishing and Presenting Share your writing with others.

Talk About It Discuss these questions with a partner or a small group of classmates. Which step in the writing process do you like the best? Which step do you think is the most challenging? Complete the sentence frames.

The step in the writing process I like best is _____

because _____
_____.

The most challenging step for me is _____
_____

because _____
_____.

ELA 1.0 Students write clear, coherent, and focused essays. The writing exhibits students' awareness of the audience and purpose. Essays contain formal introductions, supporting evidence, and conclusions. Students progress through the stages of the writing process as needed. **(ELD W B2, EI2, EI4, I5, I8, EA8)**

1 Prewriting

Prewriting is all the things you do before you begin to write. Follow the prewriting activities in the chart below. Use a separate sheet of paper for your writing. You can read the information below with a partner.

Getting Ready to Write

Choose a topic
Write down all the topic ideas you think of or brainstorm for ideas with classmates. You can also choose one of the topics from the list. Look over all your topic ideas. You may choose the one you know the most about.

Remember your audience
Your audience is the person or people who will read what you write. Is it your teacher? a friend? the principal? Knowing your audience usually changes the way you write and the words you use.

Choose a purpose
There are four main purposes for reading. They are to inform, to persuade, to entertain, and to reflect. Choose the purpose that best fits your topic.

Gather resources and information
When you gather details, you collect information on your topic. As you do this, make sure your topic is not too big or too small. Don't limit detail gathering to your own experiences and knowledge. You may need to do library research, search the Internet, or interview others to collect the information you need. Take notes on the information you will need in order to start writing.

Topic Ideas
African animals

extreme sports

fairy tale

art

natural disasters

Organize Ideas

Use the information you learned to complete this prewriting chart.

I'm Ready to Write

Topic:

Audience:

Purpose:

Resources and Information:

 ELA W 1.0 Students write clear, coherent, and focused essays. The writing exhibits students' awareness of the audience and purpose. Essays contain formal introductions, supporting evidence, and conclusions. Students progress through the stages of the writing process as needed. **ELA W 1.3** Use strategies of notetaking, outlining, and summarizing to impose structure on composition drafts. (**ELD W B2, EI2, EI6, I5, I8, EA8**) **ELA 1.4** Use organizational features of electronic text (e.g., bulletin boards, databases, keyword searches, e-mail addresses) to locate information. (**ELD W EI6, I8**)

2 Drafting

A draft is where you get all your ideas down on paper. The prewriting activities have prepared you for this, so you should do well. Take a quick look back at your topic and the details you have gathered. Focus on your main ideas, interesting details, plot and setting (if you are writing a story), and your audience.

Now, take out a sheet of paper, pick up a pencil, and start writing. The goal of a first draft is to write your paper from beginning to end. So, don't worry about mistakes. You'll have plenty of time to fix them later. Remember, even the best of writers don't expect their first draft to be perfect. The important thing about writing a draft is that it gives you something to work on—and make better.

Details, Details, Details

Make your writing clear by supporting your main ideas with enough details. Details help readers understand your ideas. If you need help adding details, you may want to use the **SEE** method.

In the **SEE** method, you start with a statement of your main idea. Then, you extend it with details that relate to the main idea. Finally, you elaborate or apply more details to the main idea. Look at the example below. The topic of this essay is how baby elephants grow to be adults.

STATEMENT   Baby elephants have a lot to learn.

EXTENSION   The baby elephant has to be taught how to use its trunk—much like a human baby has to learn how to walk or use a spoon.

ELABORATION   It takes baby elephants many years to learn how to communicate, and how to survive.

Talk About It Discuss your draft with a partner or a small group of classmates. What kind of details would you like to include in your writing that weren't there before? Complete the sentence frames.

Writing a draft was helpful because _____

_____.

I would want to add details such as _____

_____.

ELA W 1.0 Students write clear, coherent, and focused essays. The writing exhibits students' awareness of the audience and purpose. Essays contain formal introductions, supporting evidence, and conclusions. Students progress through the stages of the writing process as needed. **ELA W B2, B3, B4, B5, EI3, EI7, I8) ELA 1.1** Choose the form of writing (e.g., personal letter, letter to the editor, review, poem, report, narrative) that best suits the intended purpose. **(ELD W B4, EI3, EA1) ELA 1.2** Create multiple-paragraph expository compositions. **(ELD W B2, EI1, E12, EI4, I5, I8, EA1, EA6, EA8)**

3 Revising

You make changes when you revise. You reread your draft to find places where you need to fix what you wrote. You ask yourself questions such as the ones on the list.

As you review your writing, mark the places you need to revise. Some revisions you can write directly on your draft. If it is a word or sentence you want to change, just put a line through it. Then, write the new word or sentence above it. You can also make notes to yourself in the margins or on another sheet of paper.

When you are done, write a corrected, or revised, version of your first draft essay or story.

✓ Have I presented my ideas in the best order?

✓ Do all my paragraphs have a main idea?

✓ Did I use enough details?

✓ Do all my sentences make sense?

✓ Are there any words I want to change?

✓ Are there any details I need to take out?

✓ Are there any details I forgot to put in?

Buddy Review

As part of your revision, you can ask another person to read your writing. Ask them to tell you what they liked best about your draft, and what they liked least. Have the reader show you the places he or she may have been confused. You might even ask them if they have any suggestions for improvement. Thank them for their ideas. Then, decide what revisions you will make.

Writing Tips

Many word processing programs have built-in thesauruses to help writers improve their drafts. Highlight a word and use the thesaurus to preview a list of other words with similar meanings. Use a variety of words instead of repeating the same ones. This can make your writing more interesting.

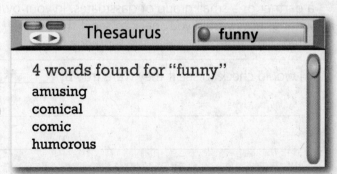

Thesaurus ● funny

4 words found for "funny"

amusing
comical
comic
humorous

ELA W 1.6 Revise writing to improve the organization and consistency of ideas within and between paragraphs. **(ELD W B2, EI7, I5, I8, EA4) ELA W 2.1** Write narratives. **ELA W 2.2** Write expository compositions (e.g., description, explanation, comparison and contrast, problem and solution.)

4 Editing and Proofreading

Once you are happy with the content of your writing, it is time to edit and proofread. That means you carefully read your writing and look for mistakes in grammar, punctuation, usage, and mechanics. Here are some things you should look for as you proofread.

Proofreading Checklist

Spelling
Use a dictionary to check the spelling of any word that you are not sure is spelled correctly.

Capitalization and Punctuation
Make sure every sentence begins with a capital letter and has a period, question mark, or exclamation point at the end. Then, look at other punctuation you have used.

Grammar and Usage Conventions
Be sure you have corrected sentence fragments and that the subject and verb of every sentence agrees.

Fact Check
Be sure the facts and ideas you include in your writing are true. Use the accuracy checklist shown on this page.

Handwriting
Make sure your handwriting is readable. Rewrite any words that may be difficult for another reader to understand.

Accuracy Checklist
✓ Names
✓ Dates and titles
✓ Statistics
✓ Exact wording of quotations
✓ Ideas that are not your own

Talk About It Discuss the Accuracy Checklist with a partner or a small group of classmates. In your own writing, how would you check to see if the items listed were true? Complete the sentence frame.

I would check to see if they were true by _____

_____

_____.

ELA LC 1.0 Students write and speak with a command of standard English conventions appropriate to the grade level. **(ELD LC B7, B8, B9) ELA 1.2** Identify and properly use indefinite pronouns and present perfect, past perfect, and future perfect verb tenses; ensure that verbs agree with compound subjects. **(ELD EI9, I10, I11, EA11, EA12) ELA 1.4** Use correct capitalization. **(ELD LC B9, EI9, EA11) ELA 1.5** Spell frequently misspelled words correctly (e.g., their, they're, there). **(ELD LC B7, B9, EI9, I10, EA11)**

5 Publishing and Presenting

Now it's time to share your writing with others.

Finalize Your Writing

You may want to type your work on a computer. This will let you make copies to share. When you use a word-processing program, choose a font that is easy to read. You might want to add pictures, drawings, diagrams, charts, or graphs to your writing. These visuals may help your readers understand your topic.

Make Your Own Portfolio

You have done a lot of hard work and it shows what you can do. Put your work in a portfolio—a folder, box, file, or a safe container. Save space in your portfolio for writing ideas, photos, and other things that inspire you.

Make a Bibliography

For some kinds of writing, you need to tell readers where you found your information. If you write a research paper, you make a bibliography to tell readers what sources you used. A bibliography follows a specific format. It tells readers the name of the title, author, and publisher of a source. It also shows what date the information was published.

> <u>Book:</u> Author's Last Name, Author's First Name. *Book Title*. Publisher's City: Publisher's Name, Year.
>
> London, Jack. *The Call of the Wild*. New York: Scholastic, 2001.
>
> <u>Magazine:</u> Author's Last Name, Author's First Name. "Article Title." *Magazine Title*. Volume Date: Page numbers.
>
> Young, Diane. "At the High End of the River." *Southern Living*. June 2000: 126-131.
>
> <u>Website:</u> "Article Title." Date accessed. URL
>
> "Circle of Stories." 25 Jan. 2006. http://www.pbs.org/circleofstories/

Writing Tips

Here are just a few suggestions for how you can share your writing. In addition to reading it to your class, you can send it to a newspaper or magazine. You can read it to your family and neighbors. You could also put it on a bulletin board in your classroom or in the school for all to see.

 ELA W 1.0 Students write clear, coherent, and focused essays. The writing exhibits students' awareness of the audience and purpose. Essays contain formal introductions, supporting evidence and conclusions. Students progress through the stages of the writing process as needed. **(ELD W B1, B4, E17, I9, EA8, EA9) ELA W 1.5** Compose documents with appropriate formatting by using word-processing skills and principles of design (e.g., margins, tabs, spacing, columns, page orientation). **(ELD W B4, E17, I9, EA9)**

Word List

- our
- are
- than
- then
- know
- now
- lose
- loose
- accept
- except

Easily Confused Words

Some words that you use are easy to confuse. They may sound almost the same or have similar spellings, but their meanings are different.

For example, the words *know* and *now* are easily confused. You probably know the difference between words like these. In writing, however, you may forget and choose the wrong one. The spell-checker in a computer program will not find this kind of error, so proofread your writing carefully.

Incorrect Spelling	Correct Spelling
<u>Are</u> friends <u>our</u> here.	<u>Our</u> friends <u>are</u> here.
<u>Than</u>, we entered the room.	<u>Then</u>, we entered the room.
I <u>now</u> that <u>know</u> is the time.	I <u>know</u> that <u>now</u> is the time.

Talk About It Study the Word List. Talk with a classmate about when you would use each word.

Practice Use words from the Word List to complete the sentences.

1. I am afraid I will _____ the ring because it is _____.

2. I can _____ all your reasons _____ the last one.

3. Jen likes the idea more now _____ she did _____.

4. _____ books _____ in the classroom.

5. The class did not _____ the schedule until _____.

ELA LC 1.5 Spell frequently misspelled words.
(ELD B9, E19, I10, EA11)

Assessment Practice

Directions Circle the letter of the sentence in which all words are spelled and used correctly.

1. A. There is a lose board in that floor.
   B. Did Jose lose the race?
   C. A screw on his glasses came lose.
   D. She neatly cut off the lose button.

2. A. This is are classroom.
   B. We waited in are classroom for a while.
   C. Are teacher came into the room.
   D. We are waiting for the teacher.

3. A. Everyone except Tina was late.
   B. Did they except your invitation?
   C. Please except my apology.
   D. We hope you will except our offer.

4. A. The baby was fussier then usual.
   B. Al would rather hike than swim.
   C. Dad wants top get home before than.
   D. The test was harder then I expected.

• •

Directions Circle the letter of the word that should be used to fill in the blank.

1. If we leave _____, we will be on time.
   A. know   B. now

2. Last year, Mr. Janzen was _____ favorite coach.
   A. are   B. our

3. If the plug comes _____, the toaster will not heat up.
   A. loose   B. lose

4. The girls got there early, but _____ they had to wait.
   A. then   B. than

5. No one will be home to _____ the delivery.
   A. except   B. accept

6. Do you _____ who won the election?
   A. know   B. now

ELA LC 1.5 Spell frequently misspelled words. (ELD B9, EI9, I10, EA11)

SP2

Spelling Handbook

Adding Suffixes

Word List
....
- edited
- admitted
- stackable
- cloudy
- lazily
- swimming
- studying
- reachable
- crying
- opened
- looking
- runny
- clumsily

Adding a suffix to a word can change its spelling. By knowing the rules, you can spell words with suffixes correctly. Take a look at the chart below to learn these rules.

Rules for Adding Suffice		
If . . .	**Then . . .**	**Example**
the word ends with a consonant followed by a y,	change the y to i.	happy + ly = happily
the word ends in y and you are adding ing,	do not change the y to i, but leave it as a y.	copy + ing = copying
the word only has one syllable and ends in a consonant,	double the last letter.	sun + y = sunny
the word has more than one syllable, and the last syllable is stressed and ends in a single consonant,	double the last letter.	begin + ing = beginning
the word has more than one syllable, and the last syllable is not stressed,	**do not** double the last letter.	remember + ed = remembered
the word ends in more than one consonant,	**never** double the last letter.	work + able = workable

. . . .

Talk About It Study the Word List. Talk with a classmate about the suffix in each word.

Practice Use words from the Word List to fill in the blanks.

1. Two words with -ly: _____

2. Two words with -ing: _____

3. Two words with two
   double consonants: _____

4. Two words with -ed: _____

5. Two words with -able: _____

ELA LC 1.0 Students write and speak with a command of standard English conventions appropriate to the grade level. **(ELD B9, EI9, I10, EA11)**

Assessment Practice

Directions Circle the letter of the word and suffix combination that is spelled correctly.

1. general + ly

   A. generaly
   B. generally
   C. generalily
   D. generaley

2. direct + ly

   A. directely
   B. directtly
   C. directly
   D. directily

3. demonstrate + ing

   A. demonstrateing
   B. demonstrating
   C. demonstratting
   D. demonstrayting

4. cancel + able

   A. cancelable
   B. cancellable
   C. canceliable
   D. cancelyable

5. pay + ing

   A. paiing
   B payying
   C. payeing
   D. paying

· ·

Directions Circle the letter of the word that is spelled correctly.

1. A. joked
   B. permited
   C. beged
   D. stoped

2. A. occurred
   B. cryed
   C. judgeing
   D. happening

3. A. abandonnment
   B. establishment
   C. developement
   D. regment

4. A. mannly
   B. likely
   C. intensly
   D. friendly

5. A. dependeable
   B. alloweable
   C. understandeable
   D. tolerable

Base Words and Endings

Some words need spelling changes when endings like *-ed* and *-ing* are added. Some words also change in their plural forms. There are several rules that can help you form words like these.

Almost all base words follow specific rules for adding *-ed* and *-ing*. There are also rules for the plural words that have irregular spelling. Take a look at the charts below to learn these rules.

Rules for Adding *-ed* and *-ing*	Correct Spelling
For most verbs, do not double the final consonant.	plant + *ed* = planted
For most one-syllable verbs that end with one vowel and one consonant, double the final consonant.	tap + *ing* = tapping
For verbs that end in a vowel + *y*, generally keep the *y*.	play + *ing* = playing
For verbs that end in a consonant + *y*, keep the y when you add *-ing*.	verify + *ing* = verifying
For verbs that end in a consonant + *y*, change the *y* to *i* when adding *-ed*.	verify + *ed* = verified

Guidelines for Spelling Irregular Plurals	Examples
For many words ending in *f*, change the *f* to *v* and add *-es*.	one wolf; three wolves
For some plurals, use the same spelling as the singular.	one moose; three moose
For some irregular plurals, add a special ending to the word.	one child; three children

Talk About It Study the Word List. Talk with a classmate. Discuss each base word and ending.

Practice First, add *-ing* to each word below to make a new word. Then, add *-ed* to each word to make another new word.

1. hurry _____

2. leak _____

3. occur _____

4. delay _____

ELA LC 1.5 Spell frequently misspelled words.
(ELD B9, EI9, I10, EA11)

Assessment Practice

Directions Circle the letter of the sentence in which the underlined word is spelled correctly.

1. A. In the past, <u>oxes</u> were used for many tasks.
   B. They pulled wagons that <u>carried</u> families to the West.
   C. If a wagon train was <u>delayied</u>, the animals waited patiently.
   D. They could travel many miles before they <u>stoped</u> to eat.

2. A. Julia spotted three <u>deers</u> in the woods.
   B. The deer <u>stoped</u> eating when they heard her approach.
   C. One of the deer had a leaf stuck in its <u>teeth</u>.
   D. Suddenly, the deer <u>leapped</u> quickly through the forest.

3. A. The clown <u>carryed</u> a huge ball in his arms.
   B. He <u>leapped</u> into the back of a silly-looking cart.
   C. Then a dog burst out of the ball he was <u>carrying</u>.
   D. The audience applauded for so long, the show was <u>delaid</u>.

4. A. Were you <u>refering</u> to us when you made that comment?
   B. You said you had <u>stoppied</u> criticizing us.
   C. We keep <u>ourselfes</u> busy and try to stay out of trouble.
   D. Is someone else <u>benefiting</u> from our hard work?

• •

Directions Apply the rules for adding endings and base words. Circle the letter of the word that is spelled correctly.

1. The mouse _____ under the table.
   A. scurryed   C. scurried
   B. scurryied   D. scurryied

2. We put three new _____ on the wall.
   A. shelfs   C. shelvies
   B. shelfves   D. shelves

3. Jack is in so much trouble that he may be _____.
   A. expeled   C. expeled
   B. expelled   D. expelied

4. Mom had been _____ about you all day.
   A. worring   C. worrying
   B. worreying   D. worryieng

5. Use that pair of _____ to cut the paper.
   A. scissors   C. scissorses
   B. scissores   D. scissor

6. They _____ many miles to reach their new home.
   A. journeyed   C. journied
   B. journeyied   D. journyied

ELA LC 1.5 Spell frequently misspelled words. (ELD B9, EI9, I10, EA11)

SP6

Spelling Handbook

Spelling Handbook

Word List

- disappoint
- misspent
- reelect
- argument
- announcement
- joyous
- stubbornness
- pitiful
- irritation
- burial

Words With Prefixes and Suffixes

Prefixes are word parts added to the beginning of base words.

Suffixes are word parts added to the end of base words.

The charts below gives you some guidelines for adding prefixes and suffixes correctly.

Adding Prefixes		
When you add a prefix,	the spelling of a base word does not change.	re + draw = redraw

Rules for Adding Suffixes		
When you add a suffix beginning with a consonant (*-ful, -tion, -ly*) to a base word that ends in a vowel + *y*,	change the y to i in the base word.	day + ly = daily
When you add a suffix beginning with a consonant (*-ful, -tion, -ly*) to a base word that ends in a consonant + *y*,	most of the time, you will not change the base word.	beauty + ful = beautiful
When you add a suffix to a base word that ends with an *e*,	drop off the e.	evaluate + *ion* = evaluation
When you add a suffix beginning with a vowel (*-al, -ion, -able*) to a base word that ends in a vowel + *y*,	change the *y* to *i* in the base word.	hurry + *ed* = hurried
When you add a suffix beginning with a vowel (*-al, -ion, -able*) to a base word that ends in a consonant + *y*,	most of the time, you will not change the base word.	play + *ing* = playing

Talk About It Study the Word List. Talk with a classmate. Discuss each prefix and suffix.

Practice Look at the Word List. Then, follow the directions.

1. Write three words with prefixes. Underline each prefix. _____

2. Write three words that have suffixes starting with vowels. Circle the word in which the spelling of the base word **does not** change. _____

3. Write four words that have suffixes starting with consonants. Circle the word that **does not** follow the guidelines. _____

ELA LC 1.5 Spell frequently misspelled words.
(ELD B9, EI9, I10, EA11)

Assessment Practice

Directions Circle the letter of the sentence in which the underlined word is spelled correctly.

1. A. We heard the <u>announcment</u> that Terry had won a scholarship.

   B. This was a <u>joyous</u> day for his parents.

   C. They always tried to help Terry and he did not want to <u>dissappoint</u> them.

   D. Hard work and <u>stubborness</u> helped him succeed.

2. A. Grandpa witnessed the <u>burial</u> of a time capsule under City Hall.

   B. He and his friend had an <u>arguement</u> about the exact day it could be opened.

   C. This became a source of great <u>irritateion</u> between them.

   D. Grandma thinks it is <u>pitifull</u>.

3. A. We do not want to <u>relect</u> him.

   B. He has <u>mispent</u> our money.

   C. His <u>stubornnness</u> is a problem.

   D. We are hoping for an <u>announcement</u>.

4. A. I don't want to <u>disapoint</u> you, but your report is not very good.

   B. In fact, it is rather <u>pityful</u>.

   C. Don't start an <u>argument</u> about it.

   D. You completely forgot to tell me about the <u>buryial</u> of the treasure chest.

. . . .

Directions Choose the correct spelling for each word.

1. A good _____ is important for success.

   A. educateion   C. educattion

   B. education   D. edicatetion

2. _____ can get you in trouble.

   A. Lazyness   C. Lazinness

   B. Lazyiness   D. Laziness

3. Please don't _____ your friends.

   A. mistreat   C. misttreat

   B. misstreat   D. misreat

4. That kitten is very _____

   A. playiful   C. playful

   B. plaiful   D. playffu

5. An _____ artist did this painting.

   A. unknown   C. unkknown

   B. unnkown   D. unown

Word List

- opposite
- separate
- cabinet
- envelope
- apologize
- calendar
- hospital
- gasoline
- courageous
- syllable

Syllables With No Sound Clues

Do you know what a **syllable** is? It is a word part that is pronounced as a separate sound. All words have at least one syllable. In words with more than one syllable (multi-syllable words), an unstressed syllable vowel sound is pronounced as a schwa – an open, neutral sound. An example of this is the beginning sound of the word *ago*.

Certain letter combinations are used to spell most long and short vowel sounds. However, the schwa sound can be spelled with almost any of the vowels. In a dictionary, the schwa sound is represented with the symbol ə.

Talk About It Study the Word List. Talk with a classmate. Discuss how to say each word, syllable by syllable.

Practice Each word from the Word List is broken into syllables, but the syllables are in the wrong order. Rearrange the syllables to spell each word correctly. Then, underline the unstressed syllable that has the schwa sound.

1. ra cou geous _____

2. i cab net _____

3. gize a pol o _____

4. pi hos tal _____

5. ble la syl _____

6. po site op _____

7. rate sep a _____

8. en cal dar _____

9. gas o line _____

10. ve lope en _____

ELA LC 1.5 Spell frequently misspelled words.
(ELD B9, EI9, I10, EA11)

Assessment Practice

Directions Circle the letter of the sentence in which the underlined word is spelled correctly.

1. A. The two tickets came in the same <u>envlaope</u>.
   B. We put them in the <u>cabenet</u>.
   C. Unfortunately, we put them in <u>seperate</u> drawers
   D. It's not <u>surprising</u> that we could only find one of them.

2. A. The company developed a new and improved <u>tracter</u>.
   B. It doesn't use a lot of <u>gasoline</u>.
   C. The <u>calender</u> for this year has a picture of the new equipment.
   D. Dad cut out the picture and hung it in the <u>gerage</u>.

3. A. For every statement you made, I think the <u>opposite</u> is true.
   B. This is not <u>suprising</u>, because we belong to different political parties.
   C. I want to <u>apoligize</u> for criticizing you.
   D. People are entitled to have <u>separite</u> opinions.

4. A. Mr. Toomey has a <u>cabinet</u> filled with old nuts, bolts, and wires.
   B. He keeps it in the back of his <u>gurage</u>.
   C. If he needs to repair his <u>tractir</u>, he has the parts he needs.
   D. His <u>slogin</u> is "Reuse, repair, recycle."

· ·

Directions Write the letter of the word that is spelled correctly.

1. Circle the date on your _____.
   A. calender   C. calandar
   B. calendar   D. calendir

2. You should _____ to your sister.
   A. apoligize   C. apologize
   B. upologize   D. apolojize

3. The book was sent in a recycled _____.
   A. envelop   C. envalope
   B. anvelope   D. envelope

4. The live on _____ ends of the park.
   A. opposite   C. apposite
   B. oppisite   D. oppasit

5. The rescue dog was very _____.
   A. courageous   C. couragis
   B. coragous   D. coregeous

6. The plastic bottles are kept _____ from the cans.
   A. seperate   C. separate
   B. separite   D. seperite

ELA LC 1.5 Spell frequently misspelled words.
(ELD B9, EI9, I10, EA11)

SP10

Word Families

A **word family** is a group of words that all share the same root. Many English word families are built around **Greek roots.** Often these root words keep the same spelling in all of the words in the word family.

The words in this list are all part of very common word families built on Greek roots. The Greek root -*tele*- means "far," -*auto*- means "self," and -*cy*- means "wheel" or "ring." The spelling of these roots does not change from word to word. If you keep this in mind, you will spell the list words and other words in the same word families correctly.

tele-	auto-	cy-
telephone	automobile	bicycle
television	automatic	cyclone
telescope	autograph	recycle
telecast		

Talk About It Study the Word List. Talk with a classmate. Discuss the Greek roots in each of the words.

Practice Read the clues below. Then, write the word from the Word List that matches each clue.

1. a two-wheeler

2. what you might want from your favorite singer

3. a program on a screen

4. the kind of screen you would show the program on

5. works by itself

6. hurricane or tornado

7. a way to talk to friends

8. four wheels and a gas pedal

9. reuse

10. a device for looking at the stars

ELA LC 1.5 Spell frequently misspelled words.
(ELD B9, EI9, I10, EA11)

Assessment Practice

Directions Circle the letter of the sentence in which the underlined word is spelled correctly.

1. A. The politician spoke on the <u>telekast</u>.
   B. He said it was important to <u>recycle</u> paper and plastic.
   C. "If you do it enough, the procedure will become <u>automatik</u>," he added.
   D. Maybe his advice could keep my room from looking like a <u>ciclone</u> hit it.

2. A. The <u>autamobile</u> was invented about 100 years ago.
   B. The <u>telefone</u> was invented even earlier.
   C. I'd like to have the <u>autograf</u> of one of these inventors.
   D. They made contact between people almost <u>automatic</u>.

3. A. We entered a contest on <u>televishion</u>.
   B. Two weeks later, we got a <u>telephone</u> call.
   C. "You have won a <u>bycyle</u>," the caller said.
   D. "Or you may choose a <u>telascope</u> instead."

4. A. A modern <u>automobeel</u> can be very fancy.
   B. For example, some even have a <u>telavision</u> in them.
   C. Maybe one day we will even be able to <u>recykle</u> gasoline.
   D. Until then, I can use less gasoline by riding a <u>bicycle</u>.

• •

Directions Circle the letter of the word that would be the correct spelling to fill in the blank.

1. They have set up a _____ on their roof.
   A. telescope   C. teleskope
   B. telascope   D. telescoap

2. A _____ is a very powerful storm.
   A. cycloan   C. cyclone
   B. ciclone   D. cicloan

3. The World Series was _____ in October.
   A. telekast   C. telicast
   B. telecast   D. telakast

4. The _____ of a famous person can be worth a lot of money.
   A. autografph   C. autigraph
   B. autograf   D. autograph

5. Our _____ is in the family room.
   A. televishon   C. television
   B. telavision   D. telivison

6. This lamp has an _____ switch.
   A. automatick   C. autamatick
   B. automatic   D. autamatic

An Introduction to Informational Text

This year you will be reading different types of informational text in your Reading and Language Arts class. These pages contain definitions and examples of the different kinds of information you will read with your teacher and classmates. If you have questions during the school year or need help understanding the purpose of various informational texts, you can refer back to these pages.

. . . .

Different Types of Informational Materials

Here are some definitions for different kinds of informational materials:

advertisement a notice designed to attract your attention and usually meant to sell a product

news article a piece of writing on a certain topic that appears in a newspaper or magazine

rental agreement or contract an official document that lets you rent or borrow something like an apartment or car, in exchange for money

warranty/insurance policy a contract that allows people to receive compensation for defects or damage to something they own

employment application a written request for a job. A listing of your personal information and work experience

business letter a formal exchange between two people about their professional interests

. . . .

Talk About It Discuss the the different types of informational materials with a partner or in a small group. Are you familiar with any of these examples? How did you learn about them? Now, complete the sentence frame.

I have read _____

because I was interested in _____

_____.

It was useful to me because _____

_____

ELA R 2.1 Identify the structural features of popular media and use the features to obtain information. **(ELD R B10, EI11, I13, EA11)**

Advertisement

An **advertisement** in print or on the web usually gives you information about a product or service. It may show a picture of the product you can buy. Often, information is provided, such as an item description and the cost. Sometimes there is a company name, address, telephone number, and web site.

Treat Your Feet to the **SALE** of the year

- Men's casual leather shoes were $75 *only $60!*
- Men and Women's boots *now $95 to $185!*
- Women's fancy leather shoes were $95 *only $49!*
- Women's casual sandals were $32 *now $25!*

> Include the **price** to help readers decide whether to buy it.

> List the **item** that will be one of the products for sale.

Walking King
SHOE STORE

Visit one of these five Chicago area locations, call 1-800-555-9330.

4533 West Bilings Avenue, Aurora, IL
Lakeview Shopping Center Evanston, IL
84 Myers Drive Lake Zurich, IL
1000 north Carroll Avenue Oaklawn, IL
345 South Silvin Downers Grove, IL

Talk About It Discuss advertisements with a partner or in a small group of classmates. Discuss other examples of advertisements. Look for ways the advertisements make the item look good to buy. How do advertisements help you decide what to buy? Complete the sentence frame with your answers. Then, work with a partner to create your own advertisement.

I was interested in buying _____

when I saw an ad for it. I liked this ad because _____

_____.

It helped me decide what to buy because _____

_____.

 ELA R 2.1 Identify the structural features of popular media and use the features to obtain information. (**ELD R B9, B10, B13, EI11, EI14, I13, EA11**)

News Article

News articles give readers information about a particular subject or area of interest, such as current events, travel, sports, or entertainment.

> The **byline** shows the name of the person who wrote the article.

> The **headline** tells you the subject of the article.

Wilson Windows to Hire 500

Robyn Corning
Benson Times Staff Writer

MORETOWN These days, most companies are cutting back. But, Wilson Windows is adding on. President Dexter W. Tiebold says workers have been putting in a lot of overtime for over a year to keep up.

"We are starting new work, and we need to hire more help. We are building on to our factory to do the new work. Once done, we will have jobs for 500 new workers."

Wilson Windows creates fancy and unusual windows and window blinds for all types of buildings. They make about 100 different kinds of windows and blinds.

"Everyone needs window coverings," said Tiebold. "This is a won-derful business because it continues to expand. We have few rivals"

Tiebold founded Wilson Windows in 1985. He started with five workers. By 1990, the company had grown to 200 workers. In 1993, Wilson Windows tore down the old factory and put in a new building. They also added 200 more people. In 2003, the company added on to the building twice and went up to 500 workers. Now, they are looking to double their workforce in 2006.

The latest addition should be done in three months. Hiring will begin in two months. About 100 people will be hired each month over the next five months. Hiring will be handled by Buxton Staffing at 423 North Derek Park Road.

> Articles may include **quotations** from people involved in the news.

Talk About It Discuss these questions with a partner or in a small group of classmates. What kinds of news stories interest you the most? Why? Complete the sentence frames with your answers.

I have read news articles on _____

_____

because I was interested in _____.

I found the articles helpful because _____.

I like to get news information from _____

because _____.

Rental Agreeement

A **rental agreement** is a document that lists the responsibilities and duties you must follow in order to rent or borrow something. It may be a **contract** for an apartment, a car, or some other product. Rental agreements are based on laws and involve an exchange of money for the product or service.

Agreement terms say what is being rented and what the expectations are.

Moonwalk Rental

Bounce Moonwalk Rental Contract

- **NUMBER OF JUMPERS**
I will watch the number of people jumping at one time.
I agree to follow these numbers and ages:

AGE	5 & under	8 & under	12 & under	Over 12
MAXIMUM NUMBER	8	6	4–5	2–3

- **SPACE**
I will meet these needs:
☐ A flat space that is 18 X 18 feet or bigger
☐ No branches or wires closer than 16 feet
☐ Space cleared of hard or sharp things and animal waste

- **SET-UP**
I understand that Bounce Moonwalk will:
☐ Put the Moonwalk up
☐ Need a 110 outlet within 100 feet
☐ Ask that an adult be present for setup

- **PAYMENT**
I agree to pay:
☐ $50 when I sign this contract
☐ $100 for 26 hours, with $15 per hour more after 26 hours.

Price The agreement lists the money owed for the rental.

- **WEATHER**
I understand that in case of bad weather, the rental can be:
☐ Moved inside
☐ Cancelled
☐ Changed to a new date

I agree to follow the rules of this contract.

Name: _____

Talk About It Discuss with a partner or in a small group of classmates. If you were to rent something, what would it be? Why? Then, discuss why agreements are important. Complete the sentence frame with your answers.

I would be interested in renting a(n) _____

because _____.

Agreements are important because _____

_____.

Informational Text and Careers Handbook

 ELA R 2.1 Identify the structural features of popular media and use the features to obtain information. **(ELD R B10, EI11, I13, EA11)**

Warranty/Insurance Policy

A **warranty** is a written guarantee that your purchase is in good condition and will be replaced or repaired if it is found defective. An **insurance policy** is a formal contract that protects a person or a piece of property and guarantees that a person will receive payment for any damages.

> This **coverage notice** shows what is paid for if injuries occur to another person or property because of an auto accident.

> **Bodily injuries** means damage or harm to a person.

> **Exclusions** What is not covered by this auto insurance policy.

PART OF AN AUTO INSURANCE POLICY

Part A—Liability Coverage

A We will agree to pay certain costs if you pay for this auto insurance. We will pay damages for bodily injury or property damage to things such as broken glass, dented fender, or broken fence. Damage because of an auto accident. Property damage includes loss of use of the damaged property. We will settle or defend any court case asking for these damages. In addition to our liability coverage, we will pay all our court costs. our duty to settle or defend a court case ends when we pay our liability coverage.

B Covered person means:
1. You or any family member living with you.
2. Any person using your covered auto. This person must have your permission to use your auto.

Other Payments

Along with our limit of liability, we will also pay to the covered person:
1. Up to $50 a day for loss of earnings.
2. 2.Other money we ask you to spend.
3. We have the right to limit payments to the covered person.

Exclusions

A We do not give Liability Coverage for any person:
1. Who chooses to cause bodily injury or property damage;
2. For damage to property owned, or being moved, or rented by the person in #1;
3. For damage to property of that person in #1.

Talk About It Discuss the question with a partner or in a small group. What kinds of things would need a warranty or an insurance policy? Complete the sentence frame with your answers. Then, talk about the different parts of the insurance policy above.

> It is important to have a warranty for products like _____
>
> _____
>
> because _____.
>
> Insurance policies are useful for products like cars and houses because
>
> _____
>
> _____

ELA R 2.1 Identify the structural features of popular media and use the features to obtain information. **(ELD R B10, B12, EI11, EI12, I13, E11)**

Employment Application

An **employment application** is a written request for a job that requires a person to provide personal background information, related work experience, and his or her reason for applying

Fill in your **personal information** so that the employer can contact you.

Indicate the position you are applying for in the **employment desired** section.

In the **work experience** part of the application, write something you've done, such as dog walking or babysitting. This section also shows where you have previously worked.

APPLICATION FOR EMPLOYMENT

Your Personal Information

Name: _____

        (Last)   *(First)*   *(Middle)*

Address: _____

_____

    E-mail Address   *Telephone*

Employment Desired _____

Date You Can Start: _____

Salary Wanted: _____

Position: _____

Education: _____

_____

Work Experience

Name and Address of Company

Date Started   *Date Left Position*

Supervisor

Why would you make a good worker?
Write two reasons below.

1. _____

2. _____

Sign Your Name _____

• •

Talk About It Discuss the question with a partner or in a small group. If you were to apply for employment, what kinds of jobs would you be interested in? Complete the sentence frame with your answers. Then, work with a partner to follow the steps and fill in the application form.

I would apply for a job doing _____

_____

because I'm interested in _____

_____

ELA R 2.5 Follow multiple-step instructions for preparing applications. **(ELD R B9, B10, EI10, I11)**

Business Letter

A **business letter** is a formal exchange in writing between two people. It is about professional or commercial interests.

One format for a business letter is called a *block style*. This is where the return address, date, closing, signature, and typed name begin at the left side of the page.

> The **inside address** is your return address.

> The **addressee** is the person who you are writing to.

> The **salutation** is a formal greeting.

> The **body** is the content of the letter.

> In the **closing,** you formally end the letter.

> Your **signature** is your full written name.

NATIONAL SPORTING GOODS
1122 West Street
Hollywood, CA 90027

June 10, 2008
Mr. Walter Jones
Springfield High School
136 School Drive
Springfield, OK 73512

Dear Mr. Jones:

We are delighted to send this letter to such a valued customer, Springfield High School.

We recently received a special shipment of top quality baseballs. As our attached brochure shows, we are offering this shipment to preferred customers at 25% off our usual price. However, you must act fast! This unusual offer is available only until July 1.

To take advantage of this special offer, call or write a letter making your request. Don't miss the opportunity to purchase these quality baseballs at such a savings!

Yours truly,

Lynda Hong
Marketing Manager
Enclosure: Brochure

Addressing an Envelope When you send someone a letter, the envelope will be the first thing the person sees. Write the complete address clearly and correctly.

Writing an Address An address has three standard lines. You may spell out words like Apartment, Avenue, and Street, or use their standard abbreviations: Apt., Ave., and St. Always use the proper abbreviation for a state, followed by the ZIP code.

An envelope has both the return address of the sender and a mailing address. If an envelope cannot be delivered for some reason, the post office will return it to the sender.

> Place your **return address** in the upper left corner.

Michelle Faber
1118 Starlight Lane
Dayton, OH 45432-3297

Ms. Joan Gillan
78 W. Taber Ave., Apt. 104
Anderson, IN 46011-1212

> Place the **address** of the person to whom you are writing at the center of the envelope.

Talk About It Discuss the questions with a partner or in a small group. Have you ever sent a formal letter to someone? Why? Complete the sentence frame with your answers. Then, work with a partner to write your own business letter and address the envelope.

I would write a business letter to _____

because _____

_____

 ELA R 2.1 Identify the structural features of popular media and use the features to obtain information. **(ELD R B10, EI11, I13, EA11)**

Instruction Manual

An **instruction manual** gives step-by-step directions for finishing a task. The instructions can explain a number of items, such as

- how to put something together
- how to do something
- how to use something

Most instructional manuals have these features:

- a description of something that the reader can do by following the directions.
- a list of the materials the reader needs.
- a series of steps explained in an order that makes sense.

8

Recording Your Announcement

Before using this answering machine, you should record the announcement (up to one minute long) that callers will hear when the system answers a call. If you choose not to record an announcement, the system answers with a prerecorded announcement: *"Hello. Please leave a message after the tone."*

1. Press and hold the ANNC button. The system beeps. Speak into the microphone, from about nine inches away. Speak normally. While you are recording, the Message Window displays the word *"RECORDING."*

2. To stop recording, release the ANNC button. The system automatically plays back your announcement.

3. To listen to your announcement again, press and release the ANNC button.

> **Step-by-step instructions** explain the order of how to use something.

Talk About It Discuss the instruction manual with a partner or in a small group of classmates. What did the instruction manual tell you to do? How were the instructions organized? Complete the sentence frame.

The instruction manual told me how to _____

_____

The instructions were organized by _____

_____

ELA R 2.5 Understand and explain the use of a simple mechanical device by following technical directions. (ELD R B9, EI10, EI11, I11, I13, EA10, EA11)

English-Spanish Glossary

How to Use This Glossary

This glossary can help you understand some of the words in this book. The entries in this glossary are in English alphabetical order. There are also guide words at the top of each page to show you the first and last words on the page. A Spanish definition appears with each English word. Each word also contains an abbreviation that tells you the part of speech. Here are the meanings for each abbreviation:

adj. = adjective   *n.* = noun
adv. = adverb   *v.* = verb

Remember, if you can't find the word you are looking for, ask for help or check a dictionary.

Cómo usar este glosario

Este glosario te puede servir para entender algunas palabras del libro. Las entradas de este glosario están en orden alfabético según el inglés. También hay palabras guía al principio de cada página para que sepas cuál es la primera y la última palabra de la página. Cada palabra aparece con una definición. También hay una abreviatura que indica de qué parte de la oración se trata. Estos son los significados de las abreviaturas:

adj. = adjetivo   *sust.* = sustantivo
adv. = adverbio   *v.* = verbo

Recuerda que si no encuentras la palabra que buscas, pide ayuda o consulta un diccionario.

• •

Aa

achieve *v.* to reach a goal
lograr *v.* alcanzar una meta

action verb *n.* a verb that shows the action of a person or thing (*cognate: verbo de acción*)
verbo de acción *sust.* verbo que indica la acción realizada por una persona o cosa

adjective *n.* a word that describes a noun or pronoun (*cognate: adjetivo*)
adjetivo *sust.* palabra que describe a un sustantivo o pronombre

admission *n.* the right to enter somewhere (*cognate: admisión*)
admisión *sust.* aceptación o permiso para entrar en un sitio

adverb *n.* a word that describes a verb, an adjective, or another adverb (*cognate: adverbio*)
adverbio *sust.* palabra que describe a un verbo, a un adjetivo o a otro adverbio

advertiser *n.* someone who makes ads, like TV commercials
anunciante *sust.* alguien que hace anuncios, como comerciales de televisión

aggression *n.* an intense energy used against someone or something (*cognate: agresión*)
agresión *sust.* energía violenta usada contra alguien o algo

alike *adv.* the same; similar in appearance
parecido *adv.* semejante; de aspecto similar

allowance *n.* money you might get for doing work at home
mesada *sust.* dinero que dan los padres a los hijos a cambio de trabajos hechos en el hogar (*regionalismo domingo, asignación mensual, paga semanal, propina*)

alternative *n.* another option or choice (*cognate: alternativa*)
alternativa *sust.* otra opción o elección

always *adv.* all the time
siempre *adv.* todo el tiempo

appearance *n.* the way someone or something looks or seems to be (*cognate: apariencia*)
apariencia *sust.* aspecto de alguien o algo; forma que parece tener alguien o algo

argue *v.* to give reasons for or against an idea
argumentar *v.* dar razones a favor o en contra de una idea

argument *n.* a reason you give for being in favor of or against something
argumento *sust.* razonamiento que se da para explicar por qué se está a favor o en contra de algo

article *n.* a special adjective; there are three articles *a, an,* and *the* (*cognate: artículo*)
artículo *sust.* adjetivo especial; hay tres artículos en inglés *a, an* y *the*

Bb

background *n.* a person's experience or knowledge; the culture and values with which a person has been raised
formación *sust.* experiencia o conocimientos de una persona; cultura y valores con los que ha sido criada una persona

battle *n.* a fight or struggle (*cognate: batalla*)
batalla *sust.* pelea o lucha

belief *n.* an important idea or opinion that you think is true
creencia *sust.* idea u opinión importante que se considera cierta

benefits *n.* positive things you receive (*cognate: beneficios*)
beneficios *sust.* cosas positivas que se reciben

birth order *n.* the order that children in a family are born
orden de nacimiento *sust.* orden en que los hijos de una misma familia han nacido

body language *n.* a nonverbal way to communicate using parts of your body
lenguaje corporal *sust.* forma no verbal de comunicarse con partes del cuerpo

brand loyalty *n.* when you buy or use the same product all the time
fidelidad a la marca *sust.* cuando usas o compras siempre el mismo producto

Cc

calculate *v.* to do math to find an answer or to plan something carefully (*cognate: calcular*)
calcular *v.* hacer operaciones matemáticas para encontrar un resultado o planificar algo cuidadosamente

captivity *n.* living in a cage, home, or zoo; not free (*cognate: cautividad*)
cautividad *sust.* vivir encerrado en un jaula, hogar o zoológico; no ser libre

cause *n.* the reason why something happens; a reason (*cognate: causa*)
causa *sust.* motivo o razón por el que sucede algo

caution *n.* a warning to be careful
advertencia *sust.* aviso de tener cuidado

challenge *n.* something that is difficult and requires extra effort to complete or do properly; *v.* facing something difficult
desafío *sust.* algo que es difícil y requiere un gran esfuerzo para hacerlo bien o para terminarlo
desafiar *v.* enfrentarse a algo difícil

characteristic *n.* a trait that describes a person or thing; a trait that is unique to a specific thing or person (*cognate: característica*)
característica *sust.* cualidad que describe a una persona o cosa; cualidad que es específica o única de esa persona o cosa

clarify *v.* to make clear (*cognate: clarificar*)
clarificar *v.* explicar algo que no está claro

class *n.* a group of students with a teacher (*cognate: clase*)
clase *sust.* grupo de estudiantes con un(a) maestro(a)

clause *n.* a group of words with its own subject and verb (*cognate: cláusula*)
cláusula *sust.* grupo de palabras con su propio sujeto y verbo

clues *n.* things that help you understand something
pistas *sust.* cosas que te ayudan a entender algo; claves

collide *v.* when two things fight or cause problems
colisionar *v.* cuando dos cosas se enfrentan o chocan

colon *n.* a punctuation mark (:) used after an independent clause for lists, time, a business letter, or on warnings and labels
dos puntos *sust.* signo de puntuación (:) usado en inglés después de una cláusula independiente, para una lista, para la hora, en una carta de negocios, o en advertencias y etiquetas

comma *n.* a punctuation mark (,) used to separate words or groups of words (*cognate: coma*)
coma *sust.* signo de puntuación (,) usado para separar palabras o grupos de palabras

common *adj.* ordinary, general; not specific; easy to find (*cognate: común*)
común *adj.* corriente, frecuente, general; no específico; fácil de encontrar

communicate *v.* to share ideas in a clear way (*cognate: comunicar*)
comunicar *v.* compartir ideas de forma clara y precisa

community *n.* a group of people who live in the same place or share similarities with each other (*cognate: comunidad*)
comunidad *sust.* grupo de personas que viven en el mismo sitio o que comparten características similares o cosas en común

comparative adjective *n.* the form of an adjective that compares two people, places, or things (*cognate: adjetivo comparativo*)
adjetivo comparativo *sust.* forma de un adjetivo que sirve para comparar dos personas, lugares o cosas

compare *v.* to show how things are alike or similar (*cognate: comparar*)
comparar *v.* mostrar en qué se parecen dos o más cosas

compete *v.* to make an effort to win (*cognate: competir*)
competir *v.* hacer un esfuerzo para ganar

complex sentence *n.* a sentence with one independent clause and one or more subordinate clauses (*cognate: oración compleja*)
oración compleja *sust.* oración con una cláusula independiente y una o más cláusulas subordinadas

compound sentence *n.* a sentence with two or more independent clauses (*cognate: oración compuesta*)
oración compuesta *sust.* oración que tiene dos o más cláusulas independientes

compound subject *n.* a subject that contains two or more subjects that share the same verb (*cognate: sujeto compuesto*)
sujeto compuesto *sust.* sujeto que contiene dos o más sujetos que comparten el mismo verbo

concept *n.* the idea you have about something based on information (*cognate: concepto*)
concepto *sust.* idea que tienes sobre algo en base a la información que dispones

conclude *v.* to use clues to figure out something not stated; to form an opinion based on evidence (*cognate: concluir*)
concluir *v.* usar claves para inferir algo que no está dicho expresamente; formarse una opinión en base a la evidencia

confirm *v.* to check to make sure something is true (*cognate: confirmar*)
confirmar *v.* revisar para asegurarse de que algo es cierto

conjunction *n.* a word that connects sentence parts (*cognate: conjunción*)
conjunción *sust.* palabra que conecta palabras o partes de oraciones

connect *v.* to link or join together (*cognate: conectar*)
conectar *v.* unir o enlazar dos o más cosas

connection *n.* a link between two things, people, or ideas (*cognate: conexión*)
conexión *sust.* unión o enlace entre dos cosas, personas o ideas

conscious *adj.* deliberate; done on purpose (*cognate: consciente*)
consciente *adj.* intencional; hecho a propósito

consequence *n.* something that follows as a result of something else (*cognate: consecuencia*)
consecuencia *sust.* algo que sucede como resultado de otra cosa

consumer *n.* someone who buys things (cognate: *consumidor*)
consumidor *sust.* alguien que compra cosas

context *n.* surrounding text or information (cognate: *contexto*)
contexto *sust.* información o texto que rodea a una palabra

contrast *v.* to show how things are different (cognate: *contrastar*)
contrastar *v.* mostrar en qué se diferencian dos cosas

convince *v.* to make someone feel sure about something (cognate: *convencer*)
convencer *v.* hacer que alguien esté seguro de algo

correspond *v.* to relate to something else; when two things are alike (cognate: *corresponder*)
corresponder *v.* estar relacionado con otra cosa; ser parecidas dos cosas

creative *adj.* able to make new ideas easily from the imagination (cognate: *creativo*)
creativo *adj.* facilidad para inventar o tener ideas usando la imaginación

culture *n.* the set of social customs, beliefs, and traits that are common among a group of people (cognate: *cultura*)
cultura *sust.* conjunto de costumbres sociales, creencias y características comunes a un grupo de personas

custom *n.* an action or habit that people take part in on a regular basis (cognate: *costumbre*)
costumbre *sust.* acción o hábito que las personas realizan regularmente

Dd

decision *n.* a choice about something (cognate: *decisión*)
decisión *sust.* elección entre dos o más opciones o acciones a seguir

declarative *adj.* a type of sentence that states an idea (cognate: *declarativa*)
declarativa *adj.* tipo de oración que enuncia o afirma una idea

defend *v.* to protect from danger (cognate: *defender*)
defender *v.* proteger del peligro

define *v.* to state the meaning (cognate: *definir*)
definir *v.* explicar el significado

demand *v.* to ask strongly for something you feel you deserve
exigir *v.* pedir enérgicamente algo que sientes que te mereces

detail *n.* a piece of information (cognate: *detalle*)
detalle *sust.* parte o fragmento específico de información

determine *v.* to decide something (cognate: *determinar*)
determinar *v.* decidir los términos de algo

devise *v.* to plan, invent, or create
idear *v.* inventar, crear o planificar algo

dialogue *n.* a conversation between two or more people (cognate: *diálogo*)
diálogo *sust.* conversación entre dos o más personas

different *adj.* not the same (cognate: *diferente*)
diferente *adj.* que no es igual

direct object *n.* a noun or pronoun that follows an action verb and answers the question *Who?* or *What?* (cognate: *objeto directo*)
objeto directo *sust.* sustantivo o pronombre que va después de un verbo de acción y responde a la pregunta *¿quién?* o *¿qué?*

direction *n.* a certain path or way (cognate: *dirección*)
dirección *sust.* rumbo o camino específico

discover *v.* to learn about something for the first time (cognate: *descubrir*)
descubrir *v.* aprender o enterarse de algo por primer vez

distinguish *v.* to tell the difference between two things (cognate: *distinguir*)
distinguir *v.* conocer o señalar las diferencias entre dos o más cosas

diverse *adj.* different from one another; various (cognate: *diverso*)
diverso *adj.* diferentes entre sí; variados

donate *v.* to give your money or your time for a cause (cognate: *donar*)
donar *v.* regalar dinero o tiempo por una causa benéfica

Ee

effect *n.* what happens next after something happens; the result (cognate: *efecto*)
efecto *sust.* lo que sucede como consecuencia de una acción o suceso; el resultado

enrichment *n.* the act of adding more to your knowledge
enriquecimiento *sust.* acción de ampliar o profundizar tus conocimientos

entertain *v.* to make happy; to amuse (cognate: *entretener*)
entretener *v.* alegrar, divertir

establish *v.* to determine; make sure of; to identify or set (cognate: *establecer*)
establecer *v.* determinar; asegurarse de algo; identificar o fijar

event *n.* what happens in a story or article
suceso *sust.* un hecho; lo que sucede en una historia o relato

evidence *n.* detail that shows that something is true (cognate: *evidencia*)
evidencia *sust.* detalle que demuestra que algo es cierto

examine *v.* to look at something very carefully (cognate: *examinar*)
examinar *v.* observar algo con mucho cuidado, fijarse en los detalles

excited *adj.* happy about something
emocionado *adj.* sentir una intensa alegría como consecuencia de algo

exclamatory *adj.* a type of sentence that expresses strong emotion (cognate: *exclamativa*)
exclamativa *adj.* tipo de oración que expresa una fuerte emoción

expectations *n.* what you think or hope will happen in the future (cognate: *expectativas*)
expectativas *sust.* lo que piensas o esperas que suceda en el futuro

experience *n.* knowledge you gain as you do something often (cognate: *experiencia*)
experiencia *sust.* conocimiento que se gana al hacer algo de forma repetida

expression *n.* an outward showing of feeling or thought (cognate: *expresión*)
expresión *sust.* demostración externa de sentimientos o pensamientos

extreme *adj.* very intense; almost dangerous (cognate: *extremo*)
extremo *adj.* muy intenso; excesivo; casi peligroso

Ff

facts *n.* pieces of information that can be proven true
hechos *sust.* información específica que es cierta y comprobable

family *n.* a group of people who are related and take care of each other (*cognate: familia*)
familia *sust.* grupo de personas que están emparentadas y que se cuidan unos a otros

fantasy *n.* something you can imagine that is not real (*cognate: fantasía*)
fantasía *sust.* algo que puedes imaginar, pero que no es real

fear *v.* to be afraid
temer *v.* tener miedo de algo

fiction *n.* not real; make-believe (*cognate: ficción*)
ficción *sust.* que no es real o verdadero; cosa imaginada

filmmaker *n.* someone who makes a movie
cineasta *sust.* persona que hace o dirige películas

focus *v.* to concentrate on one thing; to look closely at (*cognate: enfocar*)
enfocar *v.* centrarse en una cosa; observar algo

Gg

game *n.* a competition that people do for fun
juego *sust.* actividad que se hace por divertirse; competencia

gender *n.* a category that includes male and female (*cognate: género*)
género *sust.* categoría que distingue entre masculino y femenino

generation *n.* a group of people who are about the same age (*cognate: generación*)
generación *sust.* grupo de personas que tienen más o menos la misma edad

gerund *n.* a verb that ends in *-ing* and is used as a noun (*cognate: gerundio*)
gerundio *sust.* en inglés, una forma verbal que termina en *-ing*

gerund phrase *n.* a group of words that act as a gerund (*cognate: frase con gerundio*)
frase con gerundio *sust.* en inglés, grupo de palabras que funcionan como gerundio

gesture *n.* a physical movement that shows an idea or feeling (*cognate: gesto*)
gesto *sust.* movimiento físico que demuestra un sentimiento o idea

group *n.* a collection of people or things treated as a single item (*cognate: grupo*)
grupo *sust.* conjunto de personas o cosas a las que se trata como una sola entidad

guess *v.* to make an opinion without all of the information about something
adivinar *v.* llegar a una conclusión sin tener toda la información acerca de algo

Hh

hero *n.* someone who saves someone (*cognate: héroe*)
héroe *sust.* persona que salva a alguien

history *n.* an account of things that have happened in the past (*cognate: historia*)
historia *sust.* relato de eventos o hechos que han sucedido en el pasado

humor *n.* communication that is meant to be funny (*cognate: humor*)
humor *sust.* tipo de comunicación cuya intención es divertir, ser gracioso

Ii

ideals *n.* beliefs or standards of behavior that people use to decide the best way to act (*cognate: ideales*)
ideales *sust.* creencias o estándares que la gente usa como referencia para decidir cuál es la mejor forma de actuar

identify *v.* to tell what something is or who owns it; to recognize or point out (*cognate: identificar*)
identificar *v.* decir qué es algo o de quién es; reconocer o señalar

imitate *v.* to act the same way as another person (*cognate: imitar*)
imitar *v.* actuar de la misma manera que otra persona

imperative *adj.* a type of sentence that gives an order or direction (*cognate: imperativa*)
imperativa *adj.* tipo de oración que da una orden o dirección

important detail *n.* a key piece of information (*cognate: detalle importante*)
detalle importante *sust.* trozo de información clave

impossible *adj.* very hard to achieve; almost not likely to happen (*cognate: imposible*)
imposible *adj.* que no se puede hacer o lograr; que probablemente no sucederá

indefinite *adj.* not specific (*cognate: indefinido*)
indefinido *adj.* no específico

independent clause *n.* a clause with a subject and a verb that can be its own sentence (*cognate: cláusula independiente*)
cláusula independiente *sust.* cláusula que tiene sujeto y verbo y puede formar una oración por sí misma

indirect object *n.* a noun or pronoun following an action verb that answers the question *To or for whom?* or *To or for what?* (*cognate: objeto indirecto*)
objeto indirecto *sust.* nombre o pronombre que sigue a un verbo de acción, y que responde a la pregunta *¿A quién?* o *¿Para quién?*, o *¿A qué?* o *¿Para qué?*

individuality *n.* a mix of qualities that makes you different from other people (*cognate: individualidad*)
individualidad *sust.* mezcla de cualidades que te hace diferente de otros

infer *v.* to assume something based on facts (*cognate: inferir*)
inferir *v.* suponer algo basándose en hechos

influence *n.* the effect that someone or something has on you (*cognate: influencia*)
influencia *sust.* efecto que alguien o algo tiene sobre otra persona

inform *v.* to provide someone with facts and details; to communicate information or knowledge to people (*cognate: informar*)
informar *v.* proporcionar hechos, datos y detalles a alguien; comunicar información o conocimientos a otros

instructions *n.* directions telling you what to do (*cognate: instrucciones*)
instrucciones *sust.* indicaciones que informan qué hacer y cómo hacerlo

integrate *v.* to bring different parts together to make a whole (*cognate: integrar*)
integrar *v.* unir diferentes partes para hacer un todo

intense *adj.* very strong (*cognate: intenso*)
intenso *adj.* muy fuerte

intently *adv.* firmly; with a strong focus
intensamente *adv.* con mucha fuerza; atentamente

interjection *n.* a word that expresses a feeling, such as pain or excitement (*cognate: interjección*)
interjección *sust.* exclamación, palabra que expresa un sentimiento, tal como dolor o emoción

interrogative *adj.* describes a sentence that asks a question (*cognate: interrogativa*)
interrogativa *adj.* tipo de oración que hace una pregunta

invention *n.* a creation that comes from studying and experimenting (*cognate: invención*)
invención *sust.* creación que proviene de estudiar y experimentar

investigate *v.* to find out; to look at something very carefully with the goal of learning something (*cognate: investigar*)
investigar *v.* averiguar; ver y estudiar algo detenidamente con el fin de aprender algo

involve *v.* to include or be part of something (*cognate: involucrar*)
involucrar *v.* incluir o participar en algo

isolate *v.* to separate out or leave behind
aislar *v.* separar; apartar; dejar solo

issue *n.* an important concern or problem
cuestión *sust.* asunto o tema importante; problema

Jj

judge *v.* to make a decision or opinion based on facts (*cognate: juzgar*)
juzgar *v.* formarse una opinión o juicio basado en datos o hechos

justice *n.* fairness; treating all people equally (*cognate: justicia*)
justicia *sust.* equidad; tratar a las personas con imparcialidad

Kk

key *adj.* important
clave *adj.* algo que es importante

knowledge *n.* information gained when you understand certain facts, situations, or ideas; information acquired from study or through experience
conocimiento *sust.* saber obtenido al entender conceptos, hechos, situaciones o ideas; información adquirida a través del estudio o la experiencia

krumping *n.* an extreme hip-hop dance
krumping *sust.* baile callejero hip-hop

Ll

language *n.* a system used to communicate, such as words or signs
lenguaje *sust.* sistema usado para comunicar, como las palabras, los signos o los gestos

limit *n.* the point beyond which something is no longer possible (*cognate: límite*)
límite *sust.* línea imaginaria o real que separa dos cosas; que no se puede pasar o ir más allá

linking verb *n.* a verb, like *is* or *feels*, that describes a state of being
verbo copulativo *sust.* verbo en inglés, como *is* o *feels*, que indica una cualidad o estado del sujeto

logical *adj.* when something makes sense, follows the rules or is expected (*cognate: lógico*)
lógico *adj.* cuando algo tiene sentido, es razonable o es esperado

lose *v.* to fail to succeed; not win
perder *v.* no ganar; no tener éxito

Mm

main idea *n.* the topic
idea principal *sust.* el tema

manage *v.* to control something; to handle correctly (*cognate: manejar*)
manejar *v.* controlar algo; hacerse cargo de algo correctamente

manipulate *v.* to control or change (*cognate: manipular*)
manipular *v.* controlar o cambiar

marketing *n.* promoting and selling products (*cognate: mercadeo*)
mercadeo *sust.* proceso de promocionar y vender productos

meaning *n.* the definition of a word
significado *sust.* definición de una palabra

measure *v.* to find out the height, weight, or extent of something
medir *v.* averiguar la longitud, peso o extensión de una cosa

mentor *n.* an adult who guides a younger person toward success (*cognate: mentor*)
mentor *sust.* adulto que guía a una persona más joven hacia el éxito

message *n.* information you give someone in writing or in a signal (*cognate: mensaje*)
mensaje *sust.* información que se comunica a alguien, a través de palabras, signos o símbolos

method *n.* a way of doing something (*cognate: método*)
método *sust.* modo ordenado de hacer algo

migrate *v.* to travel a long distance from one place to another (*cognate: migrar*)
migrar *v.* viajar una distancia larga para permanecer un período de tiempo en otro sitio

motivate *v.* to encourage someone to achieve something (*cognate: motivar*)
motivar *v.* animar a alguien a hacer o lograr algo

multiple *adj.* more than one (*cognate: múltiple*)
múltiple *adj.* más de uno; variado

Nn

narrow *adj.* limited; not broad
estrecho *adj.* angosto, que no es ancho; limitado

negotiate *v.* to agree with discussion and to compromise (*cognate: nogociar*)
negociar *v.* acordar; conversar para llegar a un acuerdo que sirva a ambas partes

nonverbal *adj.* not using voice or language (*cognate: no verbal*)
no verbal *adj.* que no usa la voz ni el lenguaje hablado

noun *n.* a word that names a person, place, or thing
sustantivo *sust.* palabra que describe a una persona, lugar o cosa

Oo

object of the preposition *n.* the noun or pronoun in a prepositional phrase that is being related to another word in a sentence (*cognate: objeto de la preposición*)
objeto de la preposición *sust.* sustantivo o pronombre usado en una frase preposicional que se relaciona con otra palabra de la oración

observe *v.* to look closely at someone or something (*cognate: observar*)
observar *v.* examinar; mirar con atención a alguien o algo

opinion *n.* a belief based on facts and experience (*cognate: opinión*)
opinión *sust.* creencia basada en hechos y en experiencia

order *n.* the way something is arranged; sequence (*cognate: orden*)
orden *sust.* colocación de las cosas en el lugar que corresponde; secuencia

English-Spanish Glossary

overcome *v.* to solve a problem or challenge; to be successful
superar *v.* resolver un problema; tener éxito

overscheduled *adj.* when you have way too many things to do at one time
sobrecargado *adj.* cuando se tienen demasiadas cosas para hacer al mismo tiempo

Pp

paraphrase *v.* to restate in your own words (*cognate: parafrasear*)
parafrasear *v.* explicar lo que otro ha dicho con palabras diferentes

participation *n.* taking part in something with others (*cognate: participación*)
participación *sust.* tomar parte en algo con otras personas

passage *n.* a body of text (*cognate: pasaje*)
pasaje *sust.* parte o fragmento de un texto completo

pause *n.* a brief stop; *v.* to stop briefly (*cognate: pausa*)
pausa *sust.* una parada corta;
pausar *v.* parar brevemente

perfect tense *n.* a form of a verb tense that uses a form of the word *have*
tiempo perfecto *sust.* tiempo de verbo en inglés que se usa con una forma del verbo *have*

perform *v.* to act something out in public using special skills
actuar *v.* representar en público una obra de teatro, danza o música

permanent *adj.* staying in one place; not moving (*cognate: permanente*)
permanente *adj.* que no cambia; que existe siempre; que dura

personal *adj.* related to a person (*cognate: personal*)
personal *adj.* relacionado con una persona

personality *n.* the collection of emotions and behaviors that makes someone who they are (*cognate: personalidad*)
personalidad *sust.* conjunto de características de comportamiento que distinguen a una persona de otra

perspective *n.* your point of view, or the way you see and understand something (*cognate: perspectiva*)
perspectiva *sust.* punto de vista, forma en que se ve o se entiende algo

persuade *v.* to convince someone of an idea or belief; to change someone's opinion (*cognate: persuadir*)
persuadir *v.* convencer a alguien de una idea o creencia, o de hacer algo; hacer cambiar de opinión a alguien

phobia *n.* a specific kind of fear (*cognate: fobia*)
fobia *sust.* clase específica de miedo

physical comedy *n.* humor that is based on body movements (*cognate: comedia física*)
comedia física *sust.* humor basado en movimientos corporales

plural *adj.* more than one (*cognate: plural*)
plural *adj.* más de uno

positive adjective *n.* the form of an adjective that describes one person, place or thing (*cognate: adjetivo positivo*)
adjetivo positivo *sust.* forma de un adjetivo que describe a una persona, lugar o cosa

possessive *adj.* showing ownership (*cognate: posesivo*)
posesivo *adj.* que indica posesión o pertenencia

predicate adjective *n.* an adjective that describes the subject of a sentence
adjetivo predicativo *sust.* adjetivo que describe al sujeto de una oración

predicate noun *n.* a noun that renames or identifies the subject of a sentence
sustantivo predicativo *sust.* sustantivo que identifica al sujeto de una oración

predict *v.* to figure out or guess what might happen next (*cognate: predecir*)
predecir *v.* adivinar o suponer lo que puede pasar después

prepare *v.* to get ready for something before it happens (*cognate: preparar*)
preparar *v.* estar listo para algo antes de que suceda

preposition *n.* a word that relates a noun or pronoun to another word in a sentence (*cognate: preposición*)
preposición *sust.* palabra que relaciona a un sustantivo o pronombre con otra palabra en una oración

prepositional phrase *n.* a group of words that begins with a preposition and includes a noun or a pronoun (*cognate: frase preposiocional*)
frase preposicional *sust.* grupo de palabras que comienza con una preposición e incluye un sustantivo o pronombre

press *n.* organizations such as newspapers, TV news channels, and news radio stations (*cognate: prensa*)
prensa *sust.* medios informativos, como periódicos, canales televisivos de noticias y estaciones de radio de noticias

presume *v.* to expect that something will be a certain way without proof (*cognate: presumir*)
presumir *v.* esperar que algo sea de cierta manera sin tener evidencia de ello

preview *v.* to look closely at a text before you read
vistazo previo *sust.* ver un texto antes de leerlo

principal parts *n.* the four main forms of verbs (*cognate: partes principales*)
partes principales *sust.* en inglés, los cuatro formas de un verbo

privacy *n.* time or space to be left alone; opposite of public (*cognate: privacidad*)
privacidad *sust.* intimidad; tiempo o espacio para estar sólo; opuesto a público

product *n.* something that is made (*cognate: producto*)
producto *sust.* lo que se produce, fabrica o elabora

pronoun *n.* a word that replaces a noun (*cognate: pronombre*)
pronombre *sust.* palabra que reemplaza a un sustantivo

proper noun *n.* a specific person, place, or thing
sustantivo propio *sust.* sustantivo que identifica a una persona, lugar o cosa específica

prove *v.* to show that something is true
demostrar *v.* mostrar que algo es verdad

public *adj.* the opposite of private; for everyone to use (*cognate: público*)
público *adj.* lo opuesto de privado; para uso de la gente en general

punctuation *n.* the marks you see in sentences, like a *period* or a *comma* (*cognate: puntuación*)
puntuación *sust.* signos que se usan en las oraciones, como el *punto* o la *coma*

purpose *n.* reason; intention; plan (*cognate: propósito*)
propósito *sust.* objetivo, intención, plan; motivo

Qq

question *n.* a sentence that looks for an answer
pregunta *sust.* oración que busca una respuesta

quote *v.* to report something someone says
citar *v.* hacer referencia a lo que alguien ha dicho, repitiendo sus palabras

Rr

racial injustice *n.* the limiting of opportunities to people because of their race (*cognate: injusticia racial*)
injusticia racial *sust.* limitación de las oportunidades a personas debido a su origen racial

reaction *n.* something that happens in answer to something else (*cognate: reacción*)
reacción *sust.* algo que sucede como respuesta a otra cosa o estímulo

realistic *adj.* real; life-like (*cognate: realista*)
realista *adj.* parecido a la vida real

refer *v.* to direct attention to something (*cognate: referir*)
referir *v.* dirigir la atención hacia un tema

reflect *v.* to think about something; to give something serious thought (*cognate: reflexionar*)
reflexionar *v.* pensar acerca de algo; pensar seriamente sobre un tema

relationship *n.* the connection between two things (*cognate: relación*)
relación *sust.* conexión entre dos cosas o personas

rescue *v.* to save someone or something (*cognate: rescatar*)
rescatar *v.* salvar a alguien o a algo

resist *v.* to exert force (either physical or mental) against something (*cognate: resistir*)
resistir *v.* ofrecer resistencia a algo (ya sea física o mental)

resolve *v.* to deal with a problem successfully by fixing it (*cognate: resolver*)
resolver *v.* solucionar un problema

resources *n.* something that can be used for support or help (*cognate: recursos*)
recursos *sust.* algo que puede ser usado como apoyo o ayuda

respond *v.* to answer a question or do something in return (*cognate: responder*)
responder *v.* contestar a una pregunta; hacer una acción como respuesta a la acción de otra persona

responsible *adj.* behaving in a good way; following rules (*cognate: responsable*)
responsable *adj.* que cumple con sus deberes u obligaciones; que se comporta según las normas

restate *v.* to say in another way
reformular *v.* repetir algo diciéndolo de otra manera

reveal *v.* to let others know about something (*cognate: revelar*)
revelar *v.* contar algo a otras personas, especialmente algo que no se sabía o era secreto

revise *v.* to look again and correct (*cognate: revisar*)
revisar *v.* mirar otra vez, examinar y corregir los errores

reward *n.* a gift, like money, that you receive for doing something
recompensa *sust.* regalo o beneficio que se recibe a cambio de algo

risk *v.* to take a chance
arriesgar *v.* exponerse a un peligro; aventurarse a perder algo por la posibilidad de conseguir un beneficio

risky *adj.* a bit dangerous; not safe (*cognate: riesgoso*)
riesgoso *adj.* peligroso; arriesgado; inseguro

rivalry *n.* a strong or intense competition (*cognate: rivalidad*)
rivalidad *sust.* competencia fuerte o intensa entre dos personas o grupos

Ss

score *n.* music that goes with a movie or another performance
banda sonora *sust.* música que sirve de fondo a una película o actuación

self-esteem *n.* a feeling of pride in yourself (*cognate: autoestima*)
autoestima *sust.* sensación de seguridad en sí mismo; valoración de uno mismo

semicolon *n.* a punctuation mark (;) which connects two independent clauses that are closely connected in meaning
punto y coma *sust.* signo de puntuación (;) que conecta dos cláusulas independientes que están muy relacionadas por su significado

sequence *n.* the order of how events happen (*cognate: secuencia*)
secuencia *sust.* orden en el cual suceden las cosas

share *v.* to give away part of what you have
compartir *v.* regalar parte de lo que se tiene

shelter *n.* a safe place, like a home
refugio *sust.* lugar seguro, como un hogar

sibling *n.* a brother or sister
hermano/a *sust.* palabra en inglés que significa hermano o hermana

similar *adj.* alike in some way (*cognate: similar*)
similar *adj.* semejante a algo

simple *adj.* easy; not complicated (*cognate: simple*)
simple *adj.* fácil; no complicado; sencillo

simple sentence *n.* a statement with a single independent clause (*cognate: oración simple*)
oración simple *sust.* enunciado que tiene una sola cláusula independiente

simple subject *n.* the person, place or thing that a sentence is about (*cognate: sujeto simple*)
sujeto simple *sust.* persona, cosa o lugar sobre la que trata una oración

singular *adj.* one thing; not plural (*cognate: singular*)
singular *adj.* una cosa; que no es plural

skateboarding *n.* a sport that involves riding a short flat board with four wheels
montar en patineta *sust.* deporte que consiste en montar en una tabla corta sobre cuatro ruedas

skill *n.* a talent or ability to do something that makes someone special
destreza *sust.* habilidad, talento para hacer algo

source *n.* the place where something begins
fuente *sust.* origen; el lugar o cosa donde algo comienza

special effects *n.* sounds and other features that are used in movies (*cognate: efectos especiales*)
efectos especiales *sust.* sonidos e imágenes fabricados artificialmente para dar una impresión de realismo en las películas

sponsor *v.* to support something or someone with your time or money
patrocinar *v.* apoyar a algo o alguien dándole dinero o tiempo

stereotype *n.* a belief about a group of people, based on knowing only a few (*cognate: estereotipo*)
estereotipo *sust.* idea que se tiene de un grupo de personas, basándose sólo en el conocimiento que se tiene de algunos de sus miembros

study *v.* to think, read, and learn about a subject (*cognate: estudiar*)
estudiar *v.* leer, pensar y aprender sobre un tema

subject complement *n.* a noun, pronoun or adjective that appears with a linking verb
predicativo subjetivo *sust.* sustantivo, pronombre o adjetivo que aparece con un verbo copulativo

subordinate clause *n.* a clause with a subject and a verb that cannot be its own sentence (*cognate: cláusula subordinada*)
cláusula subordinada *sust.* cláusula con un sujeto y un verbo, que no puede ser una oración por sí sola

success *n.* happiness; achievement
éxito *sust.* logro; alcanzar algo

summary *n.* the main ideas in brief form
resumen *sust.* breve mención de las ideas principales

superlative adjective *n.* the form of an adjective that compares three or more people, places, or things (*cognate: adjetivo superlativo*)
adjetivo superlativo *sust.* adjetivo que compara tres o más cosas, personas o lugares

support *v.* to provide evidence for something
respaldar *v.* suministrar evidencia de algo

survey *n.* a way to gather information by asking people questions and analyzing the results
encuesta *sust.* método para recoger información de las personas haciéndoles preguntas de un cuestionario y luego analizando las respuestas

survival *n.* the act or fact of continuing to live or exist
supervivencia *sust.* hecho o acto de sobrevivir, de continuar existiendo

symbolize *v.* to represent one thing or idea (cognate: *simbolizar*)
simbolizar *v.* representar una idea o cosa

Tt

tension *n.* strong problems between people (*cognate: tensión*)
tensión *sust.* fuertes problemas entre dos o más personas

test *n.* an exam you take to check understanding
examen *sust.* prueba que se hace para comprobar el entendimiento

trend *n.* a pattern of activity or a popular style
tendencia *sust.* estilo popular; patrón de comportamiento que se repite

true *adj.* right and accurate; able to be proven; the opposite of false
cierto *adj.* verdadero, correcto; que se puede probar; lo opuesto a falso

Uu

unbelievable *adj.* unlikely to be true; impossible
increíble *adj.* que probablemente no sea cierto; imposible

unfamiliar *adj.* unknown; difficult; not easy
desconocido *adj.* extraño; algo con lo que no se ha tenido experiencia; difícil

unimportant detail *n.* a piece of information that is not essential
detalle sin importancia *sust.* trozo de información que no es esencial o relevante

unique *adj.* one of a kind, special (*cognate: único*)
único *adj.* especial, que sólo hay uno de su clase

unstructured *adj.* not having a plan or a structure (*cognate: desestructurado*)
desestructurado *adj* que no tiene una estructura clara o definida

unwanted *adj.* not wanted; not welcome
indeseado *adj.* no deseado; que no es bienvenido

urban *adj.* related to a city (*cognate: urbano*)
urbano *adj.* relacionado con la ciudad

Vv

values *n.* the ideas you believe are important (*cognate: valores*)
valores *sust.* ideas o principios que crees son importantes

verb tense *n.* the form of a verb that shows the time of the action or state of being
tiempo verbal *sust.* tiempo del verbo que indica el momento de la acción o del estado

verb *n.* a word that shows an action or a state of being (*cognate: verbo*)
verbo *sust.* palabra que indica una acción o estado

verbal *adj.* using your voice or language (*cognate: verbal*)
verbal *adj.* relacionado con la voz o el lenguaje hablado

visual *adj.* able to be seen (*cognate: visual*)
visual *adj.* que puede ser visto

volunteer *v.* to offer your time or skills for free
ofrecerse como voluntario *v.* ofrecer su tiempo y conocimientos gratuitamente

Ww

win *v.* to succeed; not lose
ganar *v.* tener éxito; no perder

Index

Index

Credits

Illustration

Background images on Reading pages by Robin Storesund
Kanaka & Yuzuru P1–P12
Scott MacNeill 16

Photographs

Every effort has been made to secure permission and provide appropriate credit for photographic material. The publisher deeply regrets any omission and pledges to correct errors called to its attention in subsequent editions.